INDEX

of

Pendle Hill Pamphlets

1934 – 2018

Request for permission to quote or to translate should be
addressed to Pendle Hill Publications, 338 Plush Mill Road,
Wallingford, PA 19086 or publications@pendlehill.org

ISBN: 978-0-87574-946-4

Designed by the Quaker Heron Press
5455 Wingborne Court
Columbia, MD 20145

September 2019 printing made possible
by the Obadiah Brown Benevolent Fund.

TABLE OF CONTENTS

(eBook available) Pendle Hill and the Quaker Heron Press embarked on a major project to make the treasures of the Pendle Hill pamphlets available world-wide as ebooks, either for the Kindle reader or the Nook platform. In the current Index by Number, a note appears to indicate whether that pamphlet is today available for download at a modest cost. To access the series, point your browser to www.amazon.com/kindle-ebooks/ or www.barnesandnoble.com/b/nook-books/ and search for your favorite title.

INTRODUCTION

Many remarkable gifts have come out of the Pendle Hill experience, but few are more remarkable than the series of Pendle Hill Pamphlets, ongoing now for more than eighty years. Conceived as the published equivalent of messages spoken in a Friends' meeting for worship, these brief essays reflect the range and vision of unprogrammed Quaker religious thought and practice.

Among the authors represented here are a handful of famous names, such as Toynbee, Weil, and Buber. But for the most part the pamphlets are the works of a "cloud of witnesses" distinguished primarily for their spirit and expressiveness. And while there are recurring themes among them (peace, worship, art), the four hundred-plus titles cover almost as many topics.

Over the years, many readers have commented on the richness of spiritual resources and information represented in these essays. Many have also asked for help in using them in study, reflection, and research. This index is designed to answer that need. It includes four sections:

Section I is an annotated list of the pamphlets. This list is in numerical order, and the pamphlet number serves as a cross-reference tool throughout the index. Each listing includes title, author, date of publication (in parentheses), a brief summary of the essay, and its subjects.

Section II groups the pamphlets alphabetically by author.

Section III lists the pamphlets alphabetically by title.

Section IV offers a subject index for the pamphlets.

INDEX BY NUMBER

1   *Cooperation and Coercion as Methods of Social Change*
Nicholson, Vincent De Witt (1934) - *(eBook available)*
The author asks if the consequences of differences and
conflicts can be creative instead of devastating.
Cooperation - Conflict Resolution - Social Concerns

2   *A Religious Solution to the Social Problem*
Brinton, Howard Haines (1934) - *(eBook available)*
A solution to the social problem of excessive individualism
will be a religious one which still respects the rights of the
individual.
Simplicity - Social Concerns

3   *The Value of Voluntary Simplicity*
Gregg, Richard Bartlett (1936) - *(eBook available)*
Voluntary simplicity involves inner and outer conditions, such
as intentional organization of life for a purpose.
Simplicity

4   *The Totalitarian Claim of the Gospels*
Willson, Dora (1939) - *(eBook available)*
When reading Jesus's teachings, one should clear the mind of
preconceptions and the interpretations of modern
psychologies, then concentrate on the Gospels' application to
practical living.
Bible - Gospels - Jesus

17 *New Nations for Old*
Boulding, Kenneth Ewart (1942) - *(eBook available)*
These plans for the abolition of war were written by an
economist-pacifist during World War II. The author looks
toward the necessary process of the redemption of
nationalism.
War - Peace

18 *Anthology with Comments*
Gray, Elizabeth Janet (1942) - *(eBook available)*
The author offers excerpts from the writings of W.H. Davies,
George Herbert, James Stephens, St. Francis of Assisi, Gerard
Manley Hopkins, Thomas Ellwood, and William Blake,
among others, with her interpretations.
Davies, W.H. - Herbert, George - Stephens, James - St.
Francis - Hopkins, Gerard - Ellwood, Thomas - Blake,
William

19 *Participation in Rural Life*
Young, Mildred Binns (1942) - *(eBook available)*
To share in the love of God, one must enter into social
responsibility for mankind.
Conduct of Life - Rural Life - Community

20 *Guide to Quaker Practice*
Brinton, Howard Haines (1943) - *(eBook available)*
The author interprets the practices of the Religious Society of
Friends in his time. Revised editions released in 1950, 1993,
and 2006.
Friends - Government - Community - Doctrine

21 *Reality of the Spiritual World*
Kelly, Thomas Raymond (1942) - *(eBook available)*
Experience a hypothetical God as if he exists, proposed Kelly
in this series of four lessons: access to spiritual reality through
the Holy Spirit in prayer, fellowship, God, and the spiritual
world.
Mysticism - Spirituality - Holy Spirit - Prayer

22 *Relief and Reconstruction: Notes on Principles Involved in Quaker Relief Service*
Wilson, Roger (1943)
Four aspects of Quaker relief work are elucidated: its religious
basis, the role of the worker, relationships between official and
voluntary organizations, and politics and sociology.
World War II - Relief Work - Service Work - Friends Service
Counsel - American Friends Service Committee

23 *Clash by Night*
Hamilton, Wallace Field (1945) - *(eBook available)*
Pacifists and militarists are portrayed as rivals in the post-war
citizenry.
Pacifism - Militarism - World War II

24 *We Are Accountable: A View of Mental Institutions*
Edelstein, Leonard Gerald (1945) - *(eBook available)*
A member of a Civilian Public Service unit in a mental
hospital during World War II describes the neglect,
mistreatment, and brutality accorded patients, with a brief
appeal to religious groups to change these conditions.
Mental Institutions - Mental Illness - Reform - Civilian
Public Service

25   *Militarism for America*
Hartman, Grover Lowell (1945)
A discussion of the pros and cons of military service, with the
author concluding there are more effective ways to create a
better society.
Conscription - Militarism - Peace

26   *The Quaker Meeting: A Personal Experience and Method
Described and Analysed*
Collier, Howard Ebenezer (1944) - *(eBook available)*
This is a revised edition of a 1944 essay on the heart and soul
of Quaker practice.
Faith and Practice - Meetings - Religious Life

27   *Sources of the Quaker Peace Testimony*
Brinton, Howard Haines (1942) - *(eBook available)*
Friends' social testimonies form a unit derived from a
common source: the direct insight of the soul into the nature
of Truth and Goodness, interpreted through Divine Light.
History - Peace - Pacifism – Testimonies

28 *Barclay in Brief: A Condensation of Robert Barclay's Apology for the True Christian Divinity. Being an Explanation and Vindication of the Principles and Doctrines of the People Called Quakers. First Published in 1676*
Barclay, Robert and Eleanore Price Mather (1942) - *(eBook available)*
For more than 200 years, Barclay's Apology was considered the most authoritative exposition of Quaker belief and practice, a synthesis of personal religious experience and the historical context of the religion. A companion to *The Inward Journey of Isaac Penington* and *William Penn's No Cross, No Crown*. With a preface by Howard H. Brinton.
Barclay, Robert - Beliefs and Testimonies - History - Theology

29 *The Inward Journey of Isaac Penington: An Abbreviation of Penington's Works*
Penington, Isaac and Robert Leach (1943) - *(eBook available)*
A condensation of the 1400-page, 1761 edition of Isaac Penington's work, with a discussion of God, free will, and justification. A companion to *Barclay in Brief* and *William Penn's No Cross, No Crown*. With a preface by Howard H. Brinton.
Doctrine - Penington, Isaac - Beliefs and Testimonies - History

30 *William Penn's No Cross, No Crown, Abridged*
Penn, William and Anna Cox Brinton (1944) - *(eBook available)*
Penn's view of conducting one's life in obedience to God. A companion to *Barclay in Brief* and *The Inward Journey of Isaac Penington*.
Penn, William - Beliefs and Testimonies - History - Conduct of Life

31 *Quakerism and India*
Alexander, Horace Gundry (1945)
An appraisal of the work of the Friends Foreign Mission Association and the Friends Ambulance Unit in India over 80 years.
India - Foreign Missions - Service Work

32 *Our Hearts are Restless*
Kilpack, Gilbert H. (1946) - *(eBook available)*
The author believes that all human life and thought depend on the first three chapters of the book of Genesis. Friends testify to these passages and address separation from the Creator.
Bible - Genesis - Doctrine

33 *Quaker Anecdotes*
Poley, Irvin C. and Ruth Verlenden Poley (1946) - *(eBook available)*
Stories that combine humor with an illustration of Quaker testimonies.
Religious Society of Friends - Humor - Proselytization - Ecumenism

34 *Contributions of the Quakers*
Gray, Elizabeth Janet (1947) - *(eBook available)*
Sections on the arrival of Quakers in America and on what
they have given to the U.S., especially in the fields of peace,
prison reform, care of the insane, education, the arts, and
respect for civil rights.
Religious Society of Friends - History - United States

35 *The Self, to the Self*
Willson, Dora (1947) - *(eBook available)*
A group of women converse about self-relationships, referring
to symbols, and listening to each other as ways to right-
relatedness. First in a series on relationships.
Self - Women - Psychology - Relationships

36 *Martha and Mary: A Woman's Relationship to Her
Home*
Benton, Josephine Moffett (1947) - *(eBook available)*
Using the Biblical story, the author finds family life, marriage,
and work make a home the right and natural place in which
to begin to enter the Kingdom of Heaven. Second in a series
on relationships.
**Home - Marriage - Family Life - Bible - Relationships -
Women - Kingdom of God**

37 *Are Your Meetings Held in the Life*
Cary, Margaret Morris (1947) - *(eBook available)*
The nature of Quaker meetings as related to daily living. Third
in a series on relationships.
**Christian Life - Family Life - Meetings - Women -
Relationships**

38   *Wide Horizon*
Brinton, Anna Cox (1947) - *(eBook available)*
Fourth in a series on relationships; a view of the world as
unified, with each person taking a responsibility.
Relationships - Community - Responsibility - Women

39   *Christianity and Civilisation*
Toynbee, Arnold Joseph (1947) - *(eBook available)*
The essay argues that human progress is interrelated with
spiritual development. (Reprinted elsewhere, but this edition
includes an introduction by the author.)
Christianity - Civilization - Western Civilization - Spirituality

40   *The Quaker Message: Extracts from Quaker Writings*
Showing the Beliefs and Practices of Quakers and the
Present Significance of Their Underlying Principles
Lucas, Sidney (1948)
The message of Quakerism in the words of representative
Quakers over 300 years, showing the vitality of the Society in
the present and future. Includes a bibliography and a detailed
index to Quaker principles.
Doctrine - Faith and Practice - Testimonies - Peace - Social
Concerns - Integrity - Truth - Education - Ministry - Inward
Light - God - Bible - Sacraments - Quakerism - Beliefs and
Testimonies

41 *Studies in Christian Enthusiasm: Illustrated from Early Quakerism*
Nuttall, Geoffrey Fillingham (1948)
Enthusiasm meant possession by deity, resulting in prophetic or poetic force. Essays are on moral, didactic, emotional, and spiritual enthusiasm.
Holy Spirit - Quakerism - History - 17th Century - Christianity

42 *The Discipline of Prayer*
Tritton, Frederick John (1948) - *(eBook available)*
Practical guidance to preliminary discipline, aspects of prayer, contemplation, intercession, and prayer in everyday life.
Prayer - Worship - Holy Spirit - Faith and Practice

43 *Standards of Success*
Havens, Teresina Rowell (1948) - *(eBook available)*
Some people try to alter conventional patterns of living; the author suggests a new criterion for success and poses questions for discussion.
Success - Values - Wealth - Poverty - Eastern Spirituality - Judaism - China - Hinduism - Japan - United States - Protestantism - Theology - Christianity

44 *The Quaker Doctrine of Inward Peace*
Brinton, Howard Haines (1948) - *(eBook available)*
Outside pressures can be met by increasing inner dimensions, inner resources, inner strength, and stability.
Inner Peace - Peace of Mind - Centering

45   *Zwischen Krieg und Frieden: Fragen zur Verständigung und Versöhnung*
Sollmann, Friedrich Wilhelm (William Frederick) (1948)
This essay offers a contribution to a democratic way of living (in German).
Democracy

46   *The Faith of an Ex-Agnostic*
Murphy, Carol R. (1949) - *(eBook available)*
The results of a search for a meaningful philosophy of religion involve the failure of science, the nature of God, commitment, and redemption.
Science - Religion - Agnosticism - Faith - God

47   *The Nature of Quakerism*
Brinton, Howard Haines (1949) - *(eBook available)*
Discusses primary, secondary, and tertiary Quaker doctrines. A revised edition of the second chapter of pamphlet #9, *Quaker Education in Theory and Practice.*
Quakerism - Doctrine - Faith and Practice - Belief - Education

48   *The Society of Friends*
Brinton, Howard Haines (1949) - *(eBook available)*
Explains the distinguishing principles of Quakerism. Reprinted from *Religion in the 20th Century,* edited by Vergilius Fern.
Quakerism - Doctrine

49   *Christ in Catastrophe: An Inward Record*
Fuchs, Emil (1949) - *(eBook available)*
A German teacher discusses living during Hitler's regime, and
out of that suffering discovering God.
**Biography - Germany - World War II - Conversion -
Imprisonment**

50   *Self-Deceit: A Comedy on Lies; A Way of Overcoming
Them*
Faber, Frederick William (1949) - *(eBook available)*
These excerpts from Faber's *Spiritual Conferences* explain self-
deceit, its varieties, characteristics, and remedies – the highest
corrective being to serve God out of personal love.
Self-Deceit - Worldliness - Vanity - Service

51   *Worship*
Woolman, John (1950) - *(eBook available)*
Excerpts from this influential Quaker's writings, edited by
Herrymon Maurer.
**Worship - Ministry - Quietism - Truth - Seeking - Woolman,
John**

52   *Search: A Personal Journey Through Chaos*
Domino, Ruth (1950) - *(eBook available)*
Reminiscences of a Pendle Hill teacher who was helped by
Quaker relief workers, then trained others to serve abroad
under the American Friends Service Committee.
**World War II - France - Germany - Refugees - American
Friends Service Committee - Relief Work - Service Work**

53 *The Power of Truth*
Maurer, Herrymon (1950) - *(eBook available)*
The author contends that truth is in all persons, offends no
one either in action or thought, loves everyone, and results in
a selfless mind.
Truth

54 *Prophetic Ministry*
Brinton, Howard Haines (1950) - *(eBook available)*
The basis of Quaker ministry is the prophetic insight arising
out of silence and delivered in brevity.
Prophecy - Christianity - Ministry

55 *The Pendle Hill Idea: An Account of a Center for Study, a
Place of Work and Worship, [and] a Quaker Experiment
in Community*
Brinton, Howard Haines (1950) - *(eBook available)*
By fusing of the divine, the liberal, the useful, and the
spiritual, the community of Pendle Hill was founded in 1930.
Community - Pendle Hill

56 *Toward Pacifism: The Convincement and Commitment of
a Young European*
Sundberg, Gunnar (1950) - *(eBook available)*
"Is pacifism on the way out?" queries a Swede who saw some
military service, took part in international work camps, lived
in Germany for a while, then became a dedicated pacifist. His
answer is no, it isn't.
Pacifism - Peace - War

57   *Atomic Peace: The Chain Reaction of Good*
Goddard, Harold Clarke (1951) - *(eBook available)*
A Shakespearean authority explores the role of imagination
and creative force, likening them to an atomic chain reaction.
With a memoir by Margaret Goddard Holt.
Imagination - Creativity

58   *Ten Questions on Prayer*
Heard, Gerald (1951) - *(eBook available)*
The whole problem of prayer involves our unavoidable
praying for others.
Prayer

59   *Quaker Strongholds*
Stephen, Caroline Emelia (1951) - *(eBook available)*
A Friend by convincement considers the basic doctrines of
Quakerism. Selections from the author's classic book on the
subject, which was first published in 1890.
Doctrine - Quakerism

60   *Promise of Deliverance: The Assurance That There Is a
Power by Which Disaster Can Be Abolished Forever*
Wilson, Dan (1951) - *(eBook available)*
A person must be regenerated by the power of God to
overcome the human condition.
Worldliness - God

61   *Guilt*
Ockel, Gerhard (1951) - *(eBook available)*
Can guilt be an aid to the progress of the spirit? An
examination of personal and collective guilt in the light of
Christian truth and modern psychology.
Guilt - Good - Evil - Sin - Psychology

62   *Toward Undiscovered Ends: Friends and Russia for 300 Years*
Brinton, Anna Cox (1951) - *(eBook available)*
An exploration of why Russia has aroused the interest of Friends for three centuries.
Russia - Quakerism - Peace - Convincement

63   *Ninth Hour*
Kilpack, Gilbert H. (1951) - *(eBook available)*
The author compares the ninth hour Christ spent on the cross to the twentieth century. With wood engravings by Fritz Eichenberg.
Christianity - 20th Century - Jesus - Eichenberg, Fritz

64   *Of Holy Disobedience*
Muste, Abraham Johannes (1952) - *(eBook available)*
The individual must be committed to Holy Disobedience against war-making and conscription.
Conscientious Objection - United States - Pacifism - Religion - Peace

65   *Reaching Decisions: The Quaker Method*
Brinton, Howard Haines (1952) - *(eBook available)*
Explains how the Religious Society of Friends answers the question, "How can a free fellowship based on Divine guidance from within set up any form of church government providing direction from without?"
Governance - Government - Sense of the Meeting - Discernment - Decision Making - Quaker Process

66 *The World in Tune*
Vining, Elizabeth Gray (1952) - *(eBook available)*
Various prayers as interpreted by this Quaker witness.
Prayer

67 *The Ministry of Counseling*
Murphy, Carol R. (1952) - *(eBook available)*
An essay on bringing together Holy Spirit and modern
therapeutic counseling.
Counseling - Pastoral Care - Psychology

68 *Art and Faith*
Eichenberg, Fritz (1952) - *(eBook available)*
Art has become an international movement, a means of
communication, and a means of experiencing the thrill of
finding God. With wood engravings by the author.
Art and Religion - Religion - Spirituality - Eichenberg, Fritz

69 *Experiment with a Life*
Collier, Howard Ebenezer (1953) - *(eBook available)*
Reflecting on his own experience, the author/physician
concludes that religion integrates wholeness with all forms of
healing.
Autobiography - Health - Religion - Healing - Wholeness

70 *Science and the Business of Living*
Vail, James Garrett (1953) - *(eBook available)*
The author shows that combining the tradition of science –
looking at obstacles as problems to be solved – and the
religious concept of moral law as the basis of our life together
could make a peaceful world.
Science - Morality - Peace

71 *Let Your Lives Speak*
Foulds, Elfrida Vipont (1953) - *(eBook available)*
In a speech at the Tercentenary Conference of the Religious
Society of Friends, an English Quaker recreates the summer of
1652.
Quakerism - History - Fox, George - Fell, Margaret - Early
Friends

72 *The Indian Testimony*
Chakravarty, Amiya Chandra (1953) - *(eBook available)*
India's philosophy of peace and the freedom movement led by
Gandhi can be the testimony of all nations. With a foreword
by Aldous Huxley.
Peace - Evil - Nonresistance - India - Gandhi

73 *The Inner Islands*
Rawlins, Winifred (1953) - *(eBook available)*
An exploration, through letters, of the challenges and
problems of living.
Christian Life

74 *Everyman's Struggle for Peace*
Alexander, Horace Gundry (1953) - *(eBook available)*
A very brief survey of Gandhi's involvement in the drive for
Indian independence based on his religious principles of soul-
force and self-rule. The author lived in India for 10 years and
knew Gandhi.
Gandhi - Peace - Social Concerns

75 *Puerto Rican Neighbor*
Schuckman, Roy (1954) - *(eBook available)*
The life of a typical *libaro* (countryman) in a *barrio* (village).
Rural Development - Puerto Rico - Rural Life

76   *McCarthyism: The Seed Is in Us*
Bristol, James E. (1954) - *(eBook available)*
Deals not only with McCarthyism, but the whole repressive
trend characterizing American life, and urges resisting every
outreach of tyranny as the early Quakers did.
Communism - McCarthyism - Red Scare - Repression - Un-
American Activities

77   *Poets Walk In*
Broomell, Anna Frances Thompson Pettit (1954) - *(eBook
available)*
Through poetry, a group of people share delight, sorrow,
searching, and understanding, thus reaching a truer sense of
poetry itself and of community.
Poetry - Community

78   *Can Quakerism Speak to the Times?*
Hobart, John Henry (1954) - *(eBook available)*
The author asks, "What is the best way to interpret Quakerism
in the modern world?"
Doctrine - Quakerism

79   *A Sense of Living*
Tonge, Mildred (1954) - *(eBook available)*
The practices of art and writing lead to a creative center in
each person.
Art and Religion - Creativity - Writing

80   *Toward Political Responsibility*
Hinshaw, Cecil Eugene (1954) - *(eBook available)*
How does man relate to the political structure of the world?
Politics - Responsibility

86   *Blake's Four-Fold Vision*
Goddard, Harold Clarke (1956) - *(eBook available)*
Innocence, experience, revolution, rebellion, and vision in
William Blake's life.
Blake, William - Literature

87   *A Shelter from Compassion*
Durr, Ruth E. (1956) - *(eBook available)*
A refuge from mankind may also be a fortification that dooms
us to weep alone. The God within us is compassion. With
wood engravings by Fritz Eichenberg.
Compassion - Eichenberg, Fritz

88   *Nonviolent Resistance: A Nation's Way to Peace*
Hinshaw, Cecil Eugene (1956) - *(eBook available)*
Addresses the problem of meeting evil on the national level.
Passive Resistance - Civil Disobedience - Peace - Evil

89   *Scruples*
Kilpack, Gilbert H. (1956) - *(eBook available)*
A scruple was originally an ancient Roman weight; then it
developed into a word meaning difficulty in deciding what is
right. This essay explores what it means to have scruples or be
scrupulous.
Morality

90   *Insured by Hope*
Young, Mildred Binns (1956) - *(eBook available)*
What are the practical means by which we can know our
single lives are bound to a greater Life and that we are secured
in hope? The author finds answers from her own experience
of poverty.
Hope - Poverty - Simplicity

91 *The Iliad: Or, The Poem of Force*
Weil, Simone (1956) - *(eBook available)*
Originally written in 1940 after the fall of France, this essay
may be read as an indirect commentary on that event, which
symbolized extreme modern force.
Force - Iliad, The - Poetry - Violence - Western Civilization
- Weil, Simone

92 *An Inward Legacy: Selections from Letters to His Friend,
Edited with an introduction by Gilbert Kilpack*
Robinson, Forbes and Gilbert Kilpack (1956) - *(eBook
available)*
These excerpts have a common theme: the force of grace,
Christian prayer, love, and revelation.
Robinson, Forbes - Spirituality - Prayer - Love - Revelation

93 *Quakerism and Other Religions*
Brinton, Howard Haines (1957) - *(eBook available)*
Meeting points and differences between Quakerism and the
major religions of China, India, and Japan.
Eastern Spirituality - India - China - Japan - Buddhism -
Hinduism - Shinto - Religion

94 *Loyalty by Oath: An Essay on the Extortion of Love*
Hoffman, Hallock B. (1957) - *(eBook available)*
The loyalty oath depends on fear for its power. The author
contends that people should be possessed by love, not fear.
Love - Oaths - Loyalty - Trust - Testimonies

95 *Inner Liberty: The Stubborn Grit in the Machine*
Viereck, Peter Robert Edwin (1957) - *(eBook available)*
Selfless sacrifice, holy pain, and the fight for the private life
are involved in the struggle of the inner imagination against
outer mechanization.
Creativity - Private Life - Liberty

96 *John Woolman and the 20th Century*
Reynolds, Reginald (1958) - *(eBook available)*
The author reflects on the thoughts of Woolman and their
applications in contemporary society.
Woolman, John - Testimonies - Spirituality

97 *The Human Way Out*
Mumford, Lewis (1958) - *(eBook available)*
The hour is late for saving the human race from the possibility
of wanton extermination or biological degradation; we must
plan with a human purpose springing from divine inspiration.
World Politics - Cold War - Nuclear War - United States -
Foreign Policy

98 *In Pursuit of Moby Dick: Melville's Image of Man*
Friedrich, Gerhard (1958) - *(eBook available)*
The paradoxical characters in this novel illustrate an age-old
faith and acts of confirmation.
Melville, Herman - Literature

99 *A Deeper Faith: The Thought of Paul Tillich*
Murphy, Carol R. (1958) - *(eBook available)*
Tillich has illuminated the situation of man in his search for
faith.
Theology - Faith - Tillich, Paul

100 *Gifts of the True Love: Based on the Old Carol "The Twelve Days of Christmas"*
Yates, Elizabeth (1958) - *(eBook available)*
Among the gifts cited are creativity, serene rest, skill in the ways of work, a sacramental approach to the daily round, faith, and courage. With illustrations by Nora S. Unwin.
Christmas - Creativity - Faith

101 *To the Refreshing of the Children of Light*
Nuttall, Geoffrey Fillingham (1959) - *(eBook available)*
An English Congregational minister sends an Open Letter to Friends.
Friends - Doctrine

102 *From One to Another*
Jacob, Norma (1959) - *(eBook available)*
Discusses the Religious Society of Friends' long-standing interest in mental illness.
History - Mental Illness - Psychology - Social Action

103 *The Character of a Quaker*
Cadbury, Henry Joel (1959) - *(eBook available)*
The successive criteria for describing a Quaker that have emerged throughout the Religious Society of Friends' history.
Doctrine - History - Quakerism

104 *Psychoanalysis and Religious Mysticism*
McClelland, David Clarence (1959)
The religious roots of psychoanalysis and its new ways of interpreting human relationships have profound meaning for Christian churches.
Mysticism - Psychology - Relationships

105 *Private Testimony and Public Policy: An Individual View of the International Predicament*
Ruopp, Phillips (1959) - *(eBook available)*
Reflections on world order and religious concerns.
World Politics - Private Life - Religion - Testimonies

106 *The Way of Man According to the Teachings of Hasidism*
Buber, Martin (1959) - *(eBook available)*
The world famous philosopher of *I and Thou* writes on Hasidism, a popular Jewish mystical movement. With a forward by Maurice Friedman.
Hasidism - Judaism - Buber, Martin

107 *Death and the Christian Answer*
Lyman, Mary Ely (1960) - *(eBook available)*
A professor of religion and ordained minister believes the Christian faith helps us to accept and not be crushed by life's ultimate denial.
Christianity - Death - Faith - Religious Life

108 *A Therapist's View of Personal Goals*
Rogers, Carl Ransom (1960) - *(eBook available)*
The questions of life's goals and purposes viewed by a humanist psychotherapist.
Psychology

109 *Another Will Gird You: A Message to the Society of Friends*
Young, Mildred Binns (1960) - *(eBook available)*
Explores questions about living a Quaker life in the modern world.
Quakerism - Religious Life

115 *Mysticism and the Experience of Love*
Thurman, Howard (1961) - *(eBook available)*
The religion of the inner life, or mysticism, is life affirming
and reaches its highest goal in love.
Inward Light - Love - Mysticism

116 *The Candle, the Lantern, the Daylight*
Young, Mildred Binns (1961) - *(eBook available)*
How the teachings of Jesus inspired the writer's life.
Christianity - Jesus - Rural Life

117 *Conscience*
Mensching, Wilhelm (1961) - *(eBook available)*
The author is a German pastor best known for his consistent
opposition to Nazism in Germany. With an introduction by
A.J. Muste.
Conscience - World War II

118 *Visible Witness: A Testimony for Radical Peace Action*
Young, Wilmer J. (1961) - *(eBook available)*
Jailed as a protester against war, the author reflects on his 70
years outside prison.
Pacifism - Conscientious Objection - Witness - Peace -
Social Action

119 *Stand Fast in Liberty*
Bristol, James E. (1961) - *(eBook available)*
Post-McCarthyism, the fear of Communism and hysteria must
be met by a program based on what we believe in, a positive
approach to the totalitarian threats of the times.
Communism - Liberty - Conscience - Social Concerns -
McCarthyism

120 *Selections on the Interior Life*
Law, William and Mary Chase Morrison (1962) - *(eBook available)*
Selections from an 18th century mystical writer who has influenced many Friends.
Mysticism - 18th Century - Prayer - Devotion - Law, William

121 *Patterns of Renewal*
Van der Post, Laurens (1962) - *(eBook available)*
The earliest human pattern is still alive and accessible to us, but modern man is cut off from experiencing this dynamic renewal deep in himself.
Anthropology - Psychology - Renewal

122 *The Civil War Diary of Cyrus Pringle, with a foreword by Henry Cadbury*
Pringle, Cyrus Guernsey and Henry Joel Cadbury (1962) - *(eBook available)*
The devotional classic of a Quaker who battled with his conscience at the time of the Civil War.
Conscientious Objection - Civil War - United States - War

123 *Prayer, the Cornerstone*
Hole, Helen Griscom Bell (1962) - *(eBook available)*
The fellowship of the first Christians had prayer as their primary experience; the author discusses prayer and its benefits.
Prayer - Christianity

124 *Saints for this Age*
Muste, Abraham Johannes (1962) - *(eBook available)*
Speaking from religious faith and a lifetime of action, the
author believes mankind must find the way into a radically
new world, a new humanity, or perish.
Christian Life

125 *Children and Solitude*
Boulding, Elise (1962) - *(eBook available)*
Is it possible to drown children in a constant flow of stimuli,
allowing no time for inward growth?
Solitude - Family Life - Children - Parenting

126 *Readiness for Religion*
Loukes, Harold (1963) - *(eBook available)*
Advice for those who seek to bring up their children to
recognize their calling as children of God.
Religious Education - Children - Family Life - Parenting

127 *Thou Dost Open Up My Life: Selections from the Rufus
Jones Collection*
Jones, Rufus Matthew and Mary Hoxie Jones (1963) - *(eBook
available)*
Readings chosen from this well-known Quaker's writings by
his daughter, Mary Hoxie Jones, from the Rufus Jones
collection at the Haverford College Library.
Jones, T. Canby - Jones, Rufus - Religious Society of
Friends - Spirituality

128 *Encounters with Art*
Blom, Dorothea Johnson (1963) - *(eBook available)*
What is great art? What can art do for us? How do we communicate with art? An expression of the author's interest in art, as well as the Jungian concept of growth and spiritual life.
Art and Religion - Jung

129 *Nonviolent Action: How It Works*
Lakey, George (1963) - *(eBook available)*
Evidently, nonviolent action has some kind of power, even when the action is not very spectacular. The question then arises, what is this power? This pamphlet discovers the "how" of nonviolent action.

Passive Resistance - Conscientious Objection - Peace - Nonviolence - Social Action

130 *Poetry Among Friends*
Thorne, Dorothy Lloyd Gilbert (1963) - *(eBook available)*
Though few Friends have been poets in the past, a growing number are being nurtured in the Quaker tradition.
Poetry - History

131 *The Dilemmas of a Reconciler: Serving the East-West Conflict*
Ullmann, Richard Karl (1963) - *(eBook available)*
The experience of reconciliation through the Christian Peace Conference of 1958 and the first all-Christian Peace Assembly of 1961.

Peace - Reconciliation - Mediation - Cold War

132 *Obstacles to Mystical Experience*
Crom, Scott (1963) - *(eBook available)*
A mathematician/philosopher discusses Western and Eastern approaches to mysticism.
Mysticism - Eckhart, Meister - Teresa of Avila - Vedanta - Hinduism - Buddhism - Eastern Spirituality

133 *The Eclipse of the Historical Jesus*
Cadbury, Henry Joel (1964) - *(eBook available)*
A Quaker religious philosopher summarizes scholarly thinking about the identity of Jesus Christ.
Jesus - History

134 *From Convincement to Conversion*
Cobin, Martin T. (1964) - *(eBook available)*
The author tells of his conversion from Judaism to Quakerism.
Friends - Convincement - Conversion

135 *The Spiritual Legacy of the American Indian*
Brown, Joseph Epes (1964) - *(eBook available)*
Written to encourage Native Americans to honor their own religious and traditional values. Selected bibliography included. With illustrations by Ann Parker.
Native Americans - Mythology - Spirituality - Indigenous Peoples

136 *The Evolutionary Potential of Quakerism*
Boulding, Kenneth Ewart (1964) - *(eBook available)*
An economist sees Quakerism as an evolutionary mutation from the main line of Christian development. He suggests that the next stage in its development is intellectual.
History - Intellectualism - Christianity

137 *Revelation and Experience*
Murphy, Carol R. (1964) - *(eBook available)*
This prolific Pendle Hill author explores faith and revelation as opposed to modern scientific positivistic philosophy.
Faith - Revelation - Religious Life

138 *An Apology for Perfection*
Hinshaw, Cecil Eugene (1964) - *(eBook available)*
The author believes the Religious Society of Friends owes more to ethical perfectionism than to mysticism.
Christian Life - Perfection

139 *Three Letters from Africa*
Brookes, Edgar Harry (1965) - *(eBook available)*
These deeply Christian letters discuss racial and social injustices and conflicts in South Africa. With an introduction by Douglas Steere and a forward by Alan Paton.
Africa - Segregation - South Africa - Race Relations

140 *A Joint and Visible Fellowship*
Snell, Beatrice Saxon (1965) - *(eBook available)*
This pamphlet addresses Friends meeting for worship and the significance of preparation for worship. With an introduction by Henry J. Cadbury.
Worship - Faith and Practice

141 *The Journal of a College Student*
Havens, Joseph (1965) - *(eBook available)*
The imagined writer reflects on contemporary student experience and religious conflict.
Religious Life - Skepticism - Youth

142 *Dear Gift of Life: A Man's Encounter with Death*
Smith, Bradford (1965) - *(eBook available)*
The author wrote this while dying of cancer, facing his own
mortality. With a forward by Mark Van Doren.
Cancer - Death - Poetry

143 *Unless One is Born Anew*
Hutchinson, Dorothy Hewitt (1965) - *(eBook available)*
The greatest challenges to face mankind are securing peace,
freedom, and bread. Individual renewal through the Seed and
the Spirit will help us address them.
Religious Society of Friends - Peace - Renewal

144 *Bethlehem Revisited*
Steere, Douglas Van (1965) - *(eBook available)*
The writer, known for his concern for the inner life, here
reflects on the Vatican and ecumenism.
Ecumenism

145 *What Doth the Lord Require of Thee?*
Young, Mildred Binns (1966) - *(eBook available)*
What does the Biblical injunction to do justly and to love
mercy require of modern man?
Inward Light - Bible - Christian Life

146 *The Wit and Wisdom of William Bacon Evans*
Brinton, Anna Cox (1966) - *(eBook available)*
Stories, anecdotes, letters, bird songs, and sonnets are linked
with a thread of biographical narrative about this distinctive
Philadelphia Friend.
Evans, William Bacon - Humor - Biography

152 *Quakerism and Christianity*
Bronner, Edwin B. (1967) - *(eBook available)*
The author addresses the question of what it means to be a Quaker today, and considers Quakerism to be the third strand of Christianity (the other two being Catholicism and Protestantism).
Doctrine - Christianity - Quakerism

153 *The Mayer/Boulding Dialogue on Peace Research*
Boulding, Kenneth Ewart and Milton Mayer (1967) - *(eBook available)*
An economist and an educator, both Quakers, debate the value of studying psychology, sociology, political science, economics, and international law as ways to peace.
Peace - International Relations - Psychology - Economics

154 *The Reality of God: Thoughts on the "Death of God" Controversy*
Purdy, Alexander Converse (1967) - *(eBook available)*
A Quaker professor of religion writes from neither a theological nor a philosophical approach, but from his study of the New Testament.
God - Christianity - Skepticism - Agnosticism - New Testament

155 *On Being Real: A Quest for Personal and Religious Wholeness*
Crom, Scott (1967) - *(eBook available)*
A conception of truth as the fidelity of consciousness to a reality that is neither fixed nor final.
Christian Life - Truth - Wholeness - Spiritual Journey

156 *Ethical Mysticism in the Society of Friends*
Brinton, Howard Haines (1967) - *(eBook available)*
The author sees ethical mysticism as a process of withdrawing
from the world and returning to it. First in a series that
includes #161, #173, and #179.
Mysticism - Ethics - Devotion

157 *Facing and Fulfilling the Later Years*
Andrews, Elsie Marion (1968) - *(eBook available)*
Creativity, travel, the interests of the mind in the world at
large, and the fluid expression of personality are positive
aspects of aging today. With a forward by Anna Cox Brinton.
Aging - Creativity

158 *Man: The Broken Image*
Murphy, Carol R. (1968) - *(eBook available)*
What can man think of man? Is he a naked ape, a thinking
reed, or a candle of the Lord? Murphy explores the human
side of the divine-human encounter.
Humanity

159 *America in Travail*
Brookes, Edgar Harry (1968) - *(eBook available)*
A visitor from South Africa sees campus unrest and the Black
Power Movement as important challenges in America in 1968.
Race Relations - Youth - Social Concerns

160 *Behind the Gospels*
Cadbury, Henry Joel (1968) - *(eBook available)*
A study of the origin of the Gospels covering historical
sequence, order of origin, relative historical value, authorship,
and other insights.
Bible - New Testament - Gospels

161 *The Religion of George Fox, 1624 - 1691, as Revealed by His Epistles*
Brinton, Howard Haines (1968) - *(eBook available)*
The author is concerned with George Fox's inner sources for outward action as revealed by his Epistles rather than his advice to early Friends on dress, speech, and behavior. Second in a series that includes #156, #173, and #179.
Fox, George - Epistles - Spirituality - Holy Spirit - Early Friends

162 *Black City Stage*
Shepherd, Jack (1968) - *(eBook available)*
A theater, film, and TV producer explores spontaneous theater.
Theater - Race Relations

163 *The Hardest Journey*
Steere, Douglas Van (1969) - *(eBook available)*
Addresses the cost of spiritual renewal and the linkage of outward with inward journeys.
Inward Light - Holy Spirit - Renewal - Spirituality - Spiritual Journey

164 *Why a Friends School? To Educate for Today's Needs*
Heath, Douglas H. (1969) - *(eBook available)*
Youth and society need the insights and vision of Quakerism and similar traditions in order to witness forcefully and creatively about how to live as a full human being.
Education - Youth - Tradition - Quakerism

165 *Gandhi Remembered*
Alexander, Horace Gundry (1969) - *(eBook available)*
A very brief survey of Gandhi's involvement in the drive for
Indian independence based on his religious principles of soul-
force and self-rule. The author lived in India for 10 years and
knew Gandhi.
Biography - Gandhi - India - Nonviolence - Liberation

166 *The Atonement of George Fox*
Fogelklou Norlind, Emilia (1969) - *(eBook available)*
The relationship between the individual and the group in
Quaker context. Edited and with an introduction by Eleanore
Price Mather.
Authority - Early Friends - Fox, George - Nayler, James

167 *William Penn: Mystic, as Reflected in His Writings*
Vining, Elizabeth Gray (1969) - *(eBook available)*
Well-known aspects of this famous Quaker, such as his
championship of religious liberty and city planning, are
contrasted with his deep mystical faith.
Penn, William - Mysticism

168 *The Modern Promethean: A Dialogue with Today's Youth*
Friedman, Maurice S. (1969) - *(eBook available)*
The author, a teacher and conscientious objector, celebrates
the Modern Job, the Problematic Rebel he sees in today's
young people, and the possibilities for a new image of man.
Youth

169 *Holy Morality: A Religious Approach to Modern Ethics*
Murphy, Carol R. (1970) - *(eBook available)*
A survey of modern moral dilemmas and ethical decisions.
Ethics - Morality

170 *Edward Hicks, Primitive Quaker: His Religion in Relation to His Art*
Mather, Eleanore Price (1970) - *(eBook available)*
The cultural and social evidences of Quakerism in Hicks's painting, with special emphasis on the inward aspect of his religion.
Hicks, Edward - Art and Religion

171 *War Resistance in Historical Perspective*
Gara, Larry (1970) - *(eBook available)*
A professor of history who was a draft resister in World War II reviews religious objection to war, war resistance as a phase of reform, and conscription since 1757 in America.
Conscientious Objection - War - History - Pacifism - Conscription

172 *Friends & the Racial Crisis*
Taylor, Richard K. (1970) - *(eBook available)*
A social worker addresses the Religious Society of Friends and its struggle against racism and poverty in America and within its own meetings.
Race Relations - Poverty

173 *Evolution and the Inward Light: Where Science and Religion Meet*
Brinton, Howard Haines (1970) - *(eBook available)*
The author reflects on the teachings of Rufus Jones and Josiah Royce, as well as the philosophies of idealism, pragmatism, and existentialism. Third in a series that includes #156, #161, and #179.
Doctrine - Inward Light - Logos - Evolution - Jones, Rufus - Royce, Josiah - Existentialism

174 *Friends, Let Us Pray*
Landstrom, Elsie H. (1970) - *(eBook available)*
The author meant not to write about prayer, but found during
writing and meditation that she must explore it.
Prayer

175 *Mutual Irradiation: A Quaker View of Ecumenism*
Steere, Douglas Van (1971) - *(eBook available)*
The author considers potential hesitations and roadblocks
which affect Friends' relationships with Christian and non-
Christian religious groups.
Ecumenism - Christianity

176 *Anna Brinton: A Study in Quaker Character*
Mather, Eleanore Price (1971) - *(eBook available)*
The life of a leading Quaker derived from her reminiscences
and those of her sister and her husband, supplemented by
other material.
Brinton, Anna and Howard - Biography

177 *Woolman and Blake: Prophets for Today*
Young, Mildred Binns (1971) - *(eBook available)*
An imaginary encounter between two men who share insights
and mercy.
Woolman, John - Blake, William - Mysticism - Quietism -
Faith - Social Concerns - Prophecy

178 *Violence or Aggressive Nonviolent Resistance?*
Moulton, Phillips P. (1971) - *(eBook available)*
Urgently needed is a large-scale program of research and
planning for genuine alternatives to military defense. This
would bring new insight and energy to nonviolent resistance.
Ethics - Violence - Nonviolence - Passive Resistance -
Social Concerns

179 *Light and Life in the Fourth Gospel*
Brinton, Howard Haines (1971) - *(eBook available)*
The philosophy and psychology of early Quakerism as derived
by John's Gospel. Fourth in a series that includes #156, #161,
and #173.
Gospel of John - Bible - New Testament - Gospels -
Doctrine - Early Friends - Inward Light

180 *Apocalypso: Revelations in Theater*
Shepherd, Jack (1971) - *(eBook available)*
Spontaneous drama is described with lists of players and
fellow-creators.
Theater - Improvisation

181 *The Quaker Message: A Personal Affirmation*
Doncaster, Leonard Hugh (1972) - *(eBook available)*
The author describes and comments on the tenets of the
Religious Society of Friends.
Doctrine - Quakerism

186 *Words & Testimonies: The Carey Memorial Lecture, Baltimore Yearly Meeting, 1971*
Silcock, Thomas Henry (1972) - *(eBook available)*
A review of the principles and special ethics of the Religious Society of Friends.
Ethics - Beliefs and Testimonies - Doctrine - Testimonies

187 *The Living Witness of John Woolman*
Moulton, Phillips P. (1973) - *(eBook available)*
The editor of Woolman's journal and essays examines the significance of this influential Quaker for modern man.
Ethics - Witness - Woolman, John

188 *Hunger for Community: An Essay on Experiential Education for Interpersonal Living*
Snoek, Jaap Diedrick (1973) - *(eBook available)*
The author explores increased sharing of our lives and deeper involvement with other persons through intentional communities, organized groups, and support groups.
Intentional Communities - Community - Education - Human Relations

189 *Simplicity: A Rich Quaker's View*
Peck, George Terhune (1973) - *(eBook available)*
The Light is the source of Friends' view of simplicity, says this historian-businessman, as he explores the implications of that testimony in his life.
Simplicity - Wealth - Stewardship - Testimonies

190 *Memories and Meditations of a Workcamper*
Richie, David S. (1973) - *(eBook available)*
Reflections on years as a participant in the first American
work camp, started in 1934.
American Friends Service Committee - Service Work

191 *Feminine Aspects of Divinity*
Lantero, Erminie Huntress (1973) - *(eBook available)*
The writer suggests that God expresses Herself/Himself in
whatever aspects, female or male, enable us to apprehend
Her/Him.
Women - Divine Feminine - God - Femininity

192 *Dialogue with the Other: Martin Buber and the Quaker
Experience*
Schroeder, Janet E. (1973) - *(eBook available)*
From a class on interreligious studies, the writer develops
conversations between man and man and between God and
man.
Buber, Martin - Judaism - God

193 *The Available Mind*
Murphy, Carol R. (1974) - *(eBook available)*
The author shows that meditation, inner quiet, the way of
nonviolence, expectancy, and humility increase available mind
and life.
Meditation - Peace of Mind

194 *Quakerism of the Future: Mystical, Prophetic, &*
Evangelical
Yungblut, John R. (1974) - *(eBook available)*
The best elements in Friends' tradition are taproots providing
vital energy and sustained motivation for the survival of faith.
Doctrine - Quakerism - Mysticism - Prophecy - Evangelism
- Renewal

195 *Quaker Worship and Techniques of Meditation*
Crom, Scott (1974) - *(eBook available)*
By combining Yoga, Transcendental Meditation, and
Quakerism, a deeper understanding of the inner life is
achieved.
Meditation - Yoga - Worship - Spiritual Practices

196 *Women and Quakerism*
Luder, Hope Elizabeth (1974) - *(eBook available)*
The lives and achievements of some remarkable women
provide striking examples of the importance of environment
in encouraging or discouraging individual achievement.
Feminism - Quakerism - History - Women - Religion

197 *Art Responds to the Bible*
Blom, Dorothea Johnson (1974) - *(eBook available)*
The author-artist uses myths, art as a language of spirit, images
of transformation from the Gospels, and 20th century
experiential religious art as generative ways of seeing and of
relating to life.
Bible - Art and Religion - Gospels - Mythology

203 *Sex and the Human Psyche: Toward a Contemporary Ethic*
Yungblut, John R. (1975) - *(eBook available)*
This essay proposes criteria for a contemporary sex ethic, hoping to stimulate thinking and ultimately, perhaps, a distinctive Friends' testimony on sex.
Sexuality - Ethics

204 *William Penn, 17th Century Founding Father: Selections from His Political Writings*
Penn, William and Edwin B. Bronner (1975) - *(eBook available)*
Selections from Penn's writings on liberty of conscience, the nature of government, peace in Europe, titles, imperial states, and a plan for the union of the American colonies.
Penn, William - Politics - Liberty - Conscience - Government - Pennsylvania - History - United States - 17th Century

205 *The Sound of Silence: Moving with T'ai Chi*
Murphy, Carol R. (1976) - *(eBook available)*
Practicing the Chinese art of meditation in movement may make a person more real and compassionate, more completely in God's world, and enable us to relate to it with serene sensitivity.
Tai Chi - Meditation - Movement Meditation

206 *Margaret Fell Speaking*
Fell, Margaret and Hugh Barbour (1976) - *(eBook available)*
Excerpts from the writings of the Mother of Quakerism, later the wife of George Fox.
Fell, Margaret - Women - Religious Society of Friends - 17th Century - History - Early Friends

207 *A Quaker Looks at Yoga*
Ackerman, Dorothy (1976) - *(eBook available)*
Combining Quaker beliefs and experience with Yogic wisdom, the author shares centering devices, adaptations for spiritual practice, special techniques for concentration, and spiritual and artistic resources as ways to enrichment.
Centering - Spiritual Practices - Yoga

208 *Rhythms of the Ecosystem*
Shetter, Janette Knott (1976) - *(eBook available)*
Developed from a course in ecology at Pendle Hill, the teacher uses the Dancing Shiva as a focus for her concerns. With illustrations by William Z. Shetter.
Cosmology - Ecology - Earthcare - Nature

209 *Philosophy of the Inner Light*
Marsh, Michael (1976) - *(eBook available)*
An economic researcher, foreign correspondent, lobbyist, and seeker, the author has found that the way out of a dogmatic disbelief in spiritual reality lies in using and understanding the inner light.
Inward Light - Holy Spirit

210 *The Psychology of a Fairy Tale*
Hart, David L. and Harriett Crosby (1977) - *(eBook available)*
The author is a Jungian analyst with a special interest in the spiritual and psychological meaning of fairy tales.
Jung - Fairy Tales - Psychology

211 *Seeking Light in the Darkness of the Unconscious*
Yungblut, John R. (1977) - *(eBook available)*
A synthesis of psychology and mysticism using Jungian approaches.
Jung - Mysticism - Psychology

212 *A Place Called Community*
Palmer, Parker J. (1977) - *(eBook available)*
The possibility of community in homes, neighborhoods, schools, places of work, or wherever people live.
Community

213 *The Triple Way: Purgation, Illumination, Union*
Peck, George Terhune (1977) - *(eBook available)*
The nature of mysticism is here explored through a three-level process.
Mysticism - Spiritual Journey

214 *Jacob Boehme: Insights into the Challenge of Evil*
Liem, Ann (1977) - *(eBook available)*
A spiritual resident of both East and West, the author sees Jacob Boehme as a Christian esoteric (like George Fox) and perhaps the most illustrious forerunner of Quakerism.
Boehme, Jacob - Evil - Good - Mysticism - Christianity - Theology

215 *Art Imagery and the Mythic Process*
Blom, Dorothea Johnson (1977)
Using mythologies of various cultures, the artist reveals processes of creativity.
Art and Religion - Mythology - Psychology - Creativity

216 *O Inward Traveller*
Murphy, Carol R. (1977) - *(eBook available)*
A spiritual journey includes approach, alternative visions, absorption, awareness, and meditation.
Meditation - Spiritual Journey

217 *Wholesight: The Spirit Quest*
Parker-Rhodes, Arthur Frederick (1978) - *(eBook available)*
Wholesight here means finding coherence among religion, science, art, and politics.
Spirituality - Science - Religion - Politics - Art and Religion - Mythology

218 *Another Way to Live: Experiencing Intentional Community*
Best, James S. (1978) - *(eBook available)*
A community is both a means and a goal; living in one is a sharing, a vision, an experiment, and a fulfillment.
Community - Intentional Communities - Movement for a New Society - Pennsylvania

219 *Approaching the Gospels*
Morrison, Mary Chase (1978) - *(eBook available)*
Intended for use in studying the life of Jesus, this is an excerpt from her leader's guide to group study of the gospels.
Bible - Gospels - Jesus

220 *A Fifth Yoga: The Way of Relationships*
Havens, Joseph (1978) - *(eBook available)*
Suggests adding the way of human relations to the four broad disciplines of Yoga.
Human Relations - Psychology - Relationships - Yoga

221 *Harnessing Pegasus: Inspiration and Meditation*
Vining, Elizabeth Gray (1978) - *(eBook available)*
The author explains how she has developed her writing style,
using the inner self, over 40 years.
Creativity - Inspiration - Meditation - Writing - Self

222 *The Family as a Way into the Future*
Boulding, Elise (1978) - *(eBook available)*
What discoveries lie before us about the family, the oldest and
longest continuing human experience?
Family Life

223 *The Roots of Pendle Hill*
Murphy, Carol R. (1979) - *(eBook available)*
Chapters in a history of Pendle Hill up to 1920, based on the
recollections of Douglas Steere, Anna and Howard Brinton,
Anna Broomell, and others. A 50th anniversary publication.
Education - History - Pendle Hill - Woolman School

224 *In the Belly of a Paradox: A Celebration of Contradictions
in the Thought of Thomas Merton*
Palmer, Parker J. (1979) - *(eBook available)*
A study of contemplation in a life of action. With a foreword
by Henri J.M. Nouwen.
Contemplation - Merton, Thomas - Paradox

225 *The Peculiar Mission of a Quaker School*
Heath, Douglas H. (1979) - *(eBook available)*
Friends schools exist to empower students, faculty, and staff to
live more fully in the Truth, to educate for goodness, and to
bring each person to the teacher within.
Education - Quakerism - Truth

226 *Homosexuality and the Bible: An Interpretation*
Barnett, Walter (1979) - *(eBook available)*
Old and New Testament citations pertaining to homosexuality
and an insightful interpretation of them by a Quaker lawyer.
Homosexuality - Bible - Sexuality

227 *Women Ministers: A Quaker Contribution*
Leach, Robert J. (1979) - *(eBook available)*
The work and influence of more than a dozen women,
beginning with Margaret Fell, in the unprogrammed tradition
of Quakerism. Edited and with an introduction by Ruth
Blattenberger.
Fell, Margaret - Ministry - Women

228 *With Thine Adversary in the Way: A Quaker Witness for
Reconciliation*
Lachmund, Margarethe (1979) - *(eBook available)*
A German Quaker writes simply of her life under Hitler's
regime and during the Russian occupation of East Germany, a
life full of meaning and peacemaking. Translated by Florence
L. Kite.
Nonviolence - Morality - Reconciliation - Witness - World
War II - Cold War

229 *Henry Hodgkin: The Road to Pendle Hill*
Greenwood, John Ormerod (1980) - *(eBook available)*
An exploration of the personality of the first director of
Pendle Hill, written for its 50th anniversary in 1980.
Hodgkin, Henry - Missionaries - Education - Biography -
Pendle Hill

230 *The Life of the Spirit in Women: A Jungian Approach*
Luke, Helen M. (1980) - *(eBook available)*
The writer believes modern women need to regain an
understanding of the feminine nature.
Women - Psychology - Jung - Femininity - Spirituality

231 *Quaker Testimonies & Economic Alternatives*
Bruyn, Severyn T. (1980) - *(eBook available)*
The Religious Society of Friends seeks a third way toward
economic choices compatible with religious principles.
Economics - Religion - Beliefs and Testimonies - Capitalism
- Socialism

232 *The Life Journey of a Quaker Artist*
Blom, Dorothea Johnson (1980) - *(eBook available)*
Teacher, writer, and artist, the author sees art as a link
between inner and outer worlds.
Art and Religion - Biography - Spiritual Journey -
Psychology

233 *Friends and the World of Nature*
Benfey, Otto Theodor (1980) - *(eBook available)*
Can we forge a new link between the insights of science and
the deeper prompting of the human spirit through a rebirth of
love for matter? A meditation on our manifold relations with
nature.
Nature - Christianity - History

238 *Lawrie Tatum, Indian Agent: Quaker Values and Hard Choices*
Hixson, Robert (1981) - *(eBook available)*
In 1869, a Quaker named Lawrie Tatum left Iowa to become an agent for the Kiowa and Comanche Indians and participate in a holy experiment. His journey is here described.
Native Americans - Government - Missionaries - Values - History - Indigenous Peoples

239 *Growing Old, a View from Within*
Jacob, Norma (1981) - *(eBook available)*
A retired social worker reflects on various aspects of aging, including its liberation, its losses, its fear, and its openings.
Aging - Psychology - Retirement

240 *Two Moral Essays: Draft for a Statement of Human Obligations and Human Personality*
Weil, Simone (1981) - *(eBook available)*
Positive morality rests on a foundation of faith. What is the nature of that faith, and what are its logical consequences? Edited and with an introduction by Ronald Hathaway.
Ethics - Morality - Weil, Simone

241 *Quakers and the Use of Power*
Lacey, Paul A. (1982) - *(eBook available)*
A reexamination of the Religious Society of Friends on the occasion of Pendle Hill's 50th Anniversary.
Power - Theology - Authority - Religion - Ethics - Religious Society of Friends

242 *The Journal and the Journey*
Morrison, Mary Chase (1982) - *(eBook available)*
The writer's interior journey of 71 years.
Spirituality - Spiritual Journey - Journaling - Writing

243 *Joel Litu, Pioneer African Quaker*
Adede, Rose (1982) - *(eBook available)*
A biographical study of the author's grandfather from
interviews, letters, speeches, and sermons.
Biography - Litu, Joel - Quakerism - Africa

244 *Reflections on Simplicity*
Prevallet, Elaine M. (1982) - *(eBook available)*
The author shares her lifelong concern with the process of
simplicity, a gift that eludes one's grasp.
Simplicity

245 *Alternative Christianity*
Punshon, John (1982) - *(eBook available)*
The writer characterizes the essence of Quakerism as radical,
charismatic, and prophetic.
Doctrine - Prophecy - Religious Society of Friends -
Christianity

246 *A Quest There Is*
Vining, Elizabeth Gray (1982) - *(eBook available)*
A collection of quotations from some of the author's favorite
mystics, with interpretive comments.
Literature - Meditation - Mysticism - Poetry

247 *The Study of War as a Contribution to Peace*
Mendl, Wolf (1983) - *(eBook available)*
Pacifists should learn to know and understand those with
whom they disagree, so that they may be bridge-builders,
nudging the world toward abandoning war.
War - Religious Life - Peace - Pacifism - International
Relations

248 *The Candle of the Lord*
Foulds, Elfrida Vipont (1983) - *(eBook available)*
Gives the reader glimpses of historic Quaker country in the
north of England and discusses the Quaker character.
Christian Life - England - History - Quakerism

249 *Speaking as One Friend to Another: On the Mystical Way
Forward*
Yungblut, John R. (1983) - *(eBook available)*
Do Quakers require a radical mutation in their consciousness?
Mysticism - Quakerism - Spirituality

250 *Jesus, Jefferson, and the Task of Friends*
Garver, Newton (1983) - *(eBook available)*
The work of the Religious Society of Friends in the world as
understood by a Christian pacifist and philosopher.
Friends - Christianity - Ethics - Jesus - Politics - Jefferson,
Thomas

251 *Nurturing Contemplation*
Murphy, Carol R. (1983) - *(eBook available)*
Quoting people who emphasize being rather than doing, the
author reflects on the fullness of the contemplative life.
Contemplation

252 *Holistic Economics and Social Protest*
Powelson, John P. (1983) - *(eBook available)*
Social protesters may not have taken into account the
complexity of economics, and this author offers explanations.
International Relations - Economics - Social Concerns

253 *Tempted by Happiness: Kazantzakis's Post-Christian
Christ*
Bien, Peter (1984) - *(eBook available)*
The author analyzes Kazantzakis's *The Last Temptation of Christ*
using a four-fold scheme devised by the novel's author, a non-
Christian, to explain evolution toward dematerialization.
Kazantzakis, Nikos - Bible - Literature - Jesus

254 *To Martin Luther King with Love: A Southern Quaker's
Tribute*
Pitre, David Wayne (1984) - *(eBook available)*
Reflects the author's years of appreciation of the writing and
faith of a Christian practicing nonviolent change and
unconditional love.
King, Martin Luther - Nonviolence - Race Relations

255 *Tending the Light*
Feagins, Mary E.B. (1984) - *(eBook available)*
The Inner Light never shines in a vacuum; it cannot function
independent of the Word and the Act.
Inward Light - Holy Spirit

256 *The Prophetic Stream*
Taber, William P. (1984) - *(eBook available)*
A call to revive the prophetic message in Quaker worship and
ministry and in Christianity.
Christianity - Doctrine - Prophecy - Worship - Ministry

257 *Artist on the Witness Stand*
Eichenberg, Fritz (1984) - *(eBook available)*
This Quaker artist, who works mostly in wood engravings,
surveys his own education and creative process. With
illustrations by the author.
Art and Religion - Creativity - Eichenberg, Fritz

258 *When Silence Becomes Singing: A Study in Perception and
Parable*
Kylin, Helen (1984) - *(eBook available)*
Metaphors and parables can become truths with the power to
transform everyday lives, connecting events to a deep place
within us and also to God. With illustrations by the author.
Art and Religion - Creativity - Metaphors - Parables -
Poetry

259 *Stewardship of Wealth*
Swayne, Kingdon W. (1985) - *(eBook available)*
Reflections on the responsibilities of being rich, with a guide
to self-assessment.
Ethics - Friends - Money - Stewardship - Wealth

260 *The Way of the Cross: The Gospel Record*
Morrison, Mary Chase (1985) - *(eBook available)*
A long-time teacher of the Gospels sees the heart of their
message as a center that is everywhere—inclusive, yet highly
individual.
Bible - Gospels

261 *Interconnections*
Prevallet, Elaine M. (1985) - *(eBook available)*
Reflections on deep relationships, the networks that God uses
to transform wounds into wholeness.
Relationships - Spirituality - Transformation - Wholeness

262 *Bearing Witness: Quaker Process and a Culture of Peace*
Cox, Gray (1985) - *(eBook available)*
Peace is portrayed as something we do, an activity of resolving
differences based on a five-stage Quaker ethic.
Peace - Quaker Process

263 *Replacing the Warrior: Cultural Ideals and Militarism*
Myers, William A. (1985) - *(eBook available)*
Examines the need for a new cultural ideal, replacing
militarism by the values shown in the life of John Woolman.
Militarism - Morality - War - Christianity - Woolman, John -
Social Concerns

264 *Leading and Being Led*
Lacey, Paul A. (1985) - *(eBook available)*
A discussion of the nature of religious leadings and where we
should be looking for them in the modern world.
Christian Life - Leadings

265 *Thoughts Are Free: A Quaker Youth Group in Nazi Germany*
Halle, Anna Sabine (1985) - *(eBook available)*
The Quaker tradition is bound up with religious belief and political action, and the author shows how these were expressed by a youth group under the Nazi regime. Translated by Mary E.B. Feagins.
History - World War II - Witness - Social Action

266 *Mending the World: Quaker Insights on the Social Order*
Boulding, Kenneth Ewart (1986) - *(eBook available)*
Learning is the key to mending the world, but it must rest on the development of a more conscious process towards human betterment: a new discipline.
Social Concerns - World Politics

267 *Encounters with Transcendence: Confessions of a Religious Philosopher*
Crom, Scott (1986) - *(eBook available)*
The author wrestles with reconciling the experience of transcendence with the disciplines of logic and mathematics.
Religion - Experience - Transcendence

268 *In God We Live*
Ostrom, Warren (1986) - *(eBook available)*
The author's journey as he finds a personal religion, culminating in joining the Religious Society of Friends.
Personal Religion - Religion - Spiritual Journey

269 *The Seed and the Tree: A Reflection on Nonviolence*
Seeger, Daniel A. (1986) - *(eBook available)*
The nonviolent sensibility understands that there is no truly beneficial, liberating, or healing politics which is not spiritual in quality; that religion and politics are one; that vision and action are one.
Nonviolence - Pacifism - Politics - Religion - Revolution - Spirituality - Social Action

270 *The Sanctuary Church*
Corbett, Jim (1986) - *(eBook available)*
A prime mover in the network bringing Central American refugees to the U.S. writes of sanctuary as a perennial task for any people that covenants to serve the Peaceable Kingdom.
Central America - Foreign Policy - Immigration - Politics - Refugees - Sanctuary Movement - Social Concerns - Witness - Indigenous Peoples - Kingdom of God

271 *Practicing Compassion for the Stranger*
Alexander, Nancy C. (1987) - *(eBook available)*
Steps in practicing compassion toward those we do not know well are described and encouraged.
Compassion - Nonviolence - Spiritual Practices

272 *Going Back: A Poet Who Was Once a Marine Returns to Vietnam*
Ehrhart, William Daniel (1987)
In search of personal healing, the author talks with many former adversaries in their austere country. He includes four poems with his reflections.
Vietnam - Poetry - War - Violence

273 *Abraham Lincoln and the Quakers*
Bassuk, Daniel Eliot (1987) - *(eBook available)*
A record of all the known stories of Lincoln and the Religious
Society of Friends, with some reflective comments by a
Quaker professor of religious studies.
History - Lincoln, Abraham - Religious Society of Friends -
United States

274 *Nonviolence on Trial*
Hillegass, Robert W. (1987) - *(eBook available)*
Nonviolent action takes place only when the principle of love
is seen as a reality grounded in Being itself, as the author has
publicly witnessed.
Nonviolence - Peace - Love

275 *The Needle's Eye: A Philippine Experience*
Urner, Carol Reilley (1987) - *(eBook available)*
Reflections on her involvement with Filipino tribal peoples
and war.
Indigenous Peoples - Nonviolence - War - Philippines

276 *Meditations on a D Major Scale*
Nicholson, Bertha May (1987) - *(eBook available)*
The author uses the theme of a D major scale to explore a
moment of truth from several perspectives: teaching and
learning, music and Quakerism, and the inward journey.
Music - Spirituality - Truth

277 *What is Quakerism? A Primer*
Peck, George Terhune (1988) - *(eBook available)*
A book for beginners on understanding the tenets of the
Religious Society of Friends.
Quakerism - Doctrine

278 *Education and the Inward Teacher*
Lacey, Paul A. (1988) - *(eBook available)*
The Inner Light, the Inward Teacher, can be a metaphor for interpreting issues in education.
Christian Life - Education - Inward Light

279 *The Apocalyptic Witness: A Radical Calling for Our Own Times*
Durland, William R. (1988) - *(eBook available)*
The author discusses living with God and living as if the Kingdom of God has already come.
Christianity - Fox, George - Prophecy - Kingdom of God

280 *An Attender at the Altar: A Sacramental Christian Responds to Silence*
Rochelle, Jay C. (1988) - *(eBook available)*
The author shows the interplay between sacrament and silence.
Sacraments - Silence

281 *A Quaker Theology of Pastoral Care: The Art of the Everyday*
White, Zoe (1988) - *(eBook available)*
By being faithful artists of the Spirit, and by creating a theology of playfulness, color, spontaneity, and surprise, one may be informed and transformed.
Pastoral Care - Theology

282 *Batter My Heart*
Ellwood, Gracia Fay (1988) - *(eBook available)*
Using ideas from biblical criticism, from psychoanalysis, and from feminist and liberation theology, the author reflects on naming a God free of caste and gender.
Abuse - Bible - Class - Domestic Violence - Feminism - Gender Relations - God - Human Relations - Liberation Theology - Psychology - Women - Theology - Violence

283 *Sink Down to the Seed*
Fardelmann, Charlotte Lyman (1989) - *(eBook available)*
A four-year journey to explore the author's inward landscape results in inner peace.
Inner Peace - Pendle Hill - Spiritual Journey

284 *Thomas R. Kelly as I Remember Him*
Jones, Thomas Canby (1988) - *(eBook available)*
The author was influenced in college by Kelly, a philosophy professor transformed into a radiant Christian.
Biography - Devotion - Kelly, Thomas R. - Spirituality

285 *Letter to a Universalist*
Punshon, John (1989) - *(eBook available)*
Written by a Christian Quaker, this pamphlet explores Universalism, Christianity, and Quaker faith and reflects the author's conviction that to establish mutual respect and tolerance among faiths is to establish world peace.
Christianity - Quakerism - Universalism - Ecumenism - Peace

286 *War Taxes: Experiences of Philadelphia Yearly Meeting Quakers through the American Revolution*
Crauderueff, Elaine J. (1989) - *(eBook available)*
A historical view of Friends' testimony regarding war taxes.
Government - History - Taxation - War - War Taxes

287 *Milestone 70*
Murphy, Carol R. (1989) - *(eBook available)*
In her 17th Pendle Hill pamphlet, the author explores her daily life in her seventieth year.
Christian Life

288 *Improvisation & Spiritual Disciplines: Continuing the Divine-Human Duet*
Conti-Entin, Carol (1989) - *(eBook available)*
The author uses musical improvisation to understand spiritual practices such as Sabbath observance, Bible reading, journal keeping, tithing, and praying.
Discipline - Improvisation - Music - Spiritual Practices

289 *To Meet at the Source: Hindus & Quakers*
Dart, Martha (1990) - *(eBook available)*
Similarities may be found in Hindu and Quaker thought in many areas that transcend language, such as pure principle, the light, unity, silence, simplicity, and guidance.
Doctrine - Ecumenism - Hinduism - Quakerism

290 *Quaker Money*
Nicholson, S. Francis (1990) - *(eBook available)*
The manager of funds for Quaker organizations and
individuals reflects on Friends and the tension between
money and ethics.
Ethics - Money - Religious Life - Stewardship - Wealth

291 *Prayer in the Contemporary World*
Steere, Douglas Van (1990) - *(eBook available)*
This deep thinker and ecumenist shares a meditation and
prayer for each day of the month.
Prayer

292 *On Hallowing One's Diminishments*
Yungblut, John R. (1990) - *(eBook available)*
A lifelong student of mysticism shares the experience of
contemplative prayer in facing many forms of diminishment:
birth defects, natural disasters, aging, and death itself.
Aging - Contemplation - Death - Disabilities - Prayer -
Religious Life - Suffering

293 *The Ministry of Presence: Without Agenda in South
Africa*
Crowe, Avis and Dyckman W. Vermilye (1990) - *(eBook
available)*
The authors share how way opened for them to become
engaged in the life of a community and Quaker meeting in
one of the world's troubled places.
Africa - Apartheid - Presence - Race Relations - Social
Concerns - South Africa

294 *Women of Power and Presence: The Spiritual Formation of Four Quaker Women Ministers*
Graham, Maureen (1990) - *(eBook available)*
A feminist studies the lives of Lucretia Coffin Mott, Elizabeth Fry, Rachel Hicks, and Rebecca Jones to discover how God moved in their lives.
Feminism - Ministry - Fry, Elizabeth - Hicks, Rachel - Jones, Rebecca - Mott, Lucretia - Women

295 *Inward Light and the New Creation: A Theological Meditation on the Center and Circumference of Quakerism*
Keiser, R. Melvin (1991) - *(eBook available)*
A theological meditation on the spirituality of George Fox's visionary journey back into Paradise and Margaret Fell's argument for women's equality in church leadership.
Equality - Feminism - Inward Light - Theology - Women - Fox, George - Fell, Margaret

296 *The Testimony of Integrity in the Religious Society of Friends*
Cooper, Wilmer Albert (1991) - *(eBook available)*
A cogent, insightful description of the central testimony among Friends from which all other testimonies evolve.
Doctrine - Faith and Practice - Honesty - Integrity - Testimonies - Truth

297 *Gospel Order: A Quaker Understanding of Faithful Church Community*
Cronk, Sandra Lee (1991) - *(eBook available)*
This essay concentrates on the communal and societal aspects of gospel order as the foundation of community life. Gospel refers to the actual relationship with God. Order refers to the patterns of daily living that flow from God.
Community - Discipline - Doctrine - Faith and Practice - Gospel Order - Religious Life

298 *The Psalms Speak*
Peck, George Terhune (1991) - *(eBook available)*
Thoughtful presentations on these ancient biblical texts bring the wisdom of the ages into our present-day experiences.
Bible - Psalms

299 *Vistas from Inner Stillness*
Walker, Richard L. (1991) - *(eBook available)*
A naturalist and astronomer writes of a knowing of God that comes from his mystical experiences of nature.
Mysticism - Spirituality - Experience - Nature

300 *Therefore Choose Life: The Spiritual Challenge of the Nuclear Age*
Tallmadge, John (1991) - *(eBook available)*
This essay renews the debate about the futility of deterrence in a post-Cold War era by introducing, as a spiritual problem, the idea of nuclear addiction and how to get out of it.
Nuclear War - Social Concerns - Spirituality

301 *Spiritual Linkage with Russians: The Story of a Leading*
Manousos, Anthony (1992) - *(eBook available)*
This essay explores the spiritual dimension of a unique
Quaker peacemaking project called *The Human Experience*, an
anthology of contemporary poetry and fiction of Russia and
the U.S., that was jointly edited and published in both
countries.
Cold War - International Relations - Peace - Leadings -
Poetry - Literature - Russia - Spirituality

302 *A Zen Buddhist Encounters Quakerism*
Tamura, Teruyasu (1992) - *(eBook available)*
A Zen Buddhist professor contrasts meditation with Quaker
worship.
Buddhism - Eastern Spirituality - Meditation - Religion -
Zen - Worship

303 *Words, Wordlessness, and the Word: Silence Reconsidered
from a Literary Point of View*
Bien, Peter (1992) - *(eBook available)*
A literary scholar considers the paradoxical relationship of
silence and words in Quaker worship, drawing on the work of
E.M. Forster, Samuel Beckett, and classical Greek writers for
insight.
Bible - Literature - Logos - Silence - Worship

304 *Mind What Stirs in Your Heart*
Havens, Teresina Rowell (1992) - *(eBook available)*
The author, inspired by Thich Nhat Hanh's walking and
breathing meditations, combines seed-verses from Quaker and
biblical writings with exercises for meditative walking.
Movement Meditation - Meditation - Spiritual Practices

305 *Spiritual Discernment: The Context and Goal of Clearness Committees*
Loring, Patricia (1992) - *(eBook available)*
This essay is grounded in the central Quaker conviction of the availability of the experience and guidance of God to every person. It addresses the challenge of distinguishing the true movement of the Spirit from the wholly human.
Clearness - Discernment - Doctrine - Leadings

306 *Four Doors to Meeting for Worship*
Taber, William P. (1992) - *(eBook available)*
A classic guide to meeting for worship. This essay describes four doors as thresholds into the heart of worship, understood as communion with the invisible—but eternal—stream of reality in which lives the eternal Christ.
Doctrine - Faith and Practice - Meeting for Worship - Quakerism - Worship

307 *Beyond Consensus: Salvaging Sense of the Meeting*
Morley, Barry (1993) - *(eBook available)*
The author discusses three essential components in discovering the sense of the meeting: release, long focus, and transition to light, all of which are nurtured by worship. Rich stories of life experiences, especially with adolescents, illustrate the process.
Clearness - Decision Making - Discernment - Doctrine - Faith and Practice - Meeting for Business - Quaker Process - Right Order - Sense of the Meeting - Unity - Worship

308 *Marriage: A Spiritual Leading for Lesbian, Gay, and Straight Couples*
Hill, Leslie (1993) - *(eBook available)*
After a summary examination of Quaker marriage practices and procedures, this essay traces the evolution of a minute on same-sex marriage in Putney Meeting in Vermont, and the marriage of two men under the meeting's care.
Family Life - Homosexuality - Leadings - Marriage - Relationships - Sexuality

309 *Universalism and Spirituality*
Hetherington, Ralph (1993) - *(eBook available)*
Bringing together material from a number of previous articles, this essay explores the nature of spirituality and its relation to universalism, with particular attention to the question of commitment to a particular religious tradition.
Spirituality - Universalism

310 *Findings: Poets and the Crisis of Faith*
Lampen, John (1993) - *(eBook available)*
The author claims poets offer confirmation to religious seekers that their glimpses of divine presence and intention are valid. Poets give them a language in which to describe such glimpses without demanding adherence to a belief system they cannot accept.
Faith - Poetry - Spirituality - Religion

311 *Without Nightfall upon the Spirit*
Morrison, Mary Chase (1993) - *(eBook available)*
Reflections on aging, including its physical, spiritual, and religious effects, by an 83-year-old author.
Aging

312 *Motions of Love: Woolman as Mystic and Activist*
Olmsted, Sterling (1993) - *(eBook available)*
A study of the interrelationship between mysticism and
activism in the life and ministry of John Woolman, as
reflected in his writings.
History - Love - Mysticism - Social Action - Woolman, John

313 *Friends and Alcohol: Recovering a Forgotten Testimony*
Levering, Robert (1994) - *(eBook available)*
After examining the history of Friends' corporate witness on
the use of alcoholic beverages, which for the most part
produced a call for total abstinence, the author argues that
Friends should reexamine and reclaim this testimony.
Alcohol - Testimonies

314 *Spiritual Hospitality: A Quaker's Understanding of
Outreach*
Gillman, Harvey (1994) - *(eBook available)*
The author elevates three fundamental principles for
outreach: 1) There is something sacred in each person; 2) how
we relate to people is what we actually believe about them; and
3) how we treat others is our personal statement about God.
Community - Hospitality - Membership - Outreach -
Spirituality

315 *Answering That of God in Our Children*
Heath, Harriet (1994) - *(eBook available)*
The stories in this pamphlet, drawn from life, illustrate the
wondering that children do and the need for guidance it
opens for any who live and work with them.
Children - Family Life - Parenting - Religious Education

316 *For That Solitary Individual: An Octogenarian's Counsel on Living and Dying*
Yungblut, John R. (1994) - *(eBook available)*
The author defines three activities of evolution: differentiation, interiority, and communion. He counsels each person to seek a contemplative life to nurture these activities.
Contemplation - Death

317 *The Kingdom and the Way: Meditations on the Kingdom of God*
Urner, Carol Reilley (1994) - *(eBook available)*
The author shares specific biblical texts and her meditations, connecting the inward holy place where she meets God with Buddhist teachings and the fundamental truths of Christian experience.
Bible - Buddhism - Christianity - Gospels - Jesus - Meditation - Kingdom of God

318 *Silence: Our Eye on Eternity*
Seeger, Daniel A. (1994) - *(eBook available)*
This essay is a reflection on the practice of inner silence in everyday life.
Contemplation - Silence - Spiritual Practices

319 *Stories from Kenya*
Gates, Thomas and Liz Gates (1995) - *(eBook available)*
Relates stories which arose out of the authors' experiences of living and working at a Quaker mission hospital in rural western Kenya.
Africa - Autobiography - Kenya - Missionaries - Service Work

320 *Leadership Among Friends*
McDonald, Ron (1995) - *(eBook available)*
The author looks at the ambivalence toward authority among
Quaker youth, the need for common experiences of depth,
and ways of encouraging more inspired ministry.
**Authority - Community - Discernment - Leadership -
Ministry - Youth**

321 *No Royal Road to Reconciliation*
Knudsen-Hoffman, Gene (1995) - *(eBook available)*
The author sees wounds in the perpetrator as the source of
violence. This essay describes the nature and healing of
trauma and offers a view of health that can move us to
listening, forgiveness, compassion, and reconciliation.
**Compassion - Forgiveness - Healing - Health -
Reconciliation - Violence - Social Action**

322 *Nonviolence and Community: Reflections on the
Alternatives to Violence Project*
Garver, Newton and Eric Reitan (1995) - *(eBook available)*
Nonviolence requires a spirit that comes from within which
no curriculum can create or implant. The authors describe
how the Alternatives to Violence Project (AVP) organizes
experiences to draw forth that spirit and how doing so builds
supportive community.
**Alternatives to Violence Project - Community - Justice -
Nonviolence - Prison - Reconciliation - Social Action**

323 *An Experiment in Faith: Quaker Women Transcending Differences*
Abbott, Margery Post (1995) - *(eBook available)*
Tells of the author's journey of discovering Evangelical Friends. In the process she comes to terms with a fuller understanding of Quakerism as experienced by others and experiences God's presence, opening her to unexpected depths in her own faith.
Evangelical Quakerism - Ecumenism - Faith - Religious Society of Friends - Spirituality

324 *Traveling In*
Steere, Douglas Van (1995) - *(eBook available)*
"I am going to speak about 'traveling in' and about my own personal journey. I haven't done that on any other occasion in quite so full a way as I'm going to do here this morning." So begins this essay, a treasure from one of Quakerism's most thoughtful writers. Edited by E. Glenn Hinson.
Autobiography - Religion - Spiritual Journey - Spirituality

325 *The Unconscious*
Murphy Jr, Robert Cushman (1996) - *(eBook available)*
A doctor shares his career as physician/psychiatrist and his wisdom on how the unconscious works to fulfill longings, leading to greater health for those who are able to trust the Guide.
Psychology - Religion - Spirituality

326 *Liberation Theology for Quakers*
Lynd, Alice and Staughton (1996) - *(eBook available)*
A record of the authors effort to live out the convictions of
liberation theology nonviolently. Friends are invited to
become a group that serves the poor directly, seeking
passionately to create a new society.
**Liberation - Liberation Theology - Poverty - Psychology -
Religious Life - Social Action - Spirituality - Theology**

327 *Depression and Spiritual Growth*
Mihalas, Dimitri (1996) - *(eBook available)*
The author writes, "In 1986 I passed through a year of major
depression, the worst experience of my life, yet I have reaped
incalculable benefits from it. My world view has changed
radically for the better. My life now opens out on peaceful
paths and breathtaking vistas I never knew existed."
Depression - Mental Illness - Psychology - Spirituality

328 *The Servant Church*
Elford, Ricardo and Jim Corbett (1996) - *(eBook available)*
The authors write as a Catholic priest and a Quaker pagan
whose separate paths have converged in a Jewish view of
religion. For the prophetic faith, religion is about faithful
service that is grounded in a covenant community's allegiance
to the Peaceable Kingdom.
**Sanctuary Movement - Social Concerns - Religious Life -
Kingdom of God**

329 *There Is a Fountain: A Quaker Life in Process*
Horn, Helen Steere (1996) - *(eBook available)*
A life story about renewal, commitment, faith, doubt, success,
defeat, and a balance of activism and contemplation.
Autobiography - Social Concerns - Spirituality

330 *Searching for the Real Jesus*
Warren, Roland Leslie (1997) - *(eBook available)*
The early Friends, as Publishers of Truth, proclaimed they had experienced the Truth of God's presence. The author, a Quaker with reverence for scripture, explains the thinking of prominent contemporary scholars who debate the historical veracity of Jesus.
Bible - History - Jesus - Literature

331 *Communion for a Quaker*
Bieber, Nancy (1997) - *(eBook available)*
In the words of the author, "This is the story of a journey in search of the sacrament of communion... I ask my questions, and find, not only answers, but also a challenge for all of us, the challenge of daily sacramental living."
Christian Life - Communion - Sacraments - Spiritual Practices

332 *The Burning One-ness Binding Everything: A Spiritual Journey*
Birchard, Bruce (1997) - *(eBook available)*
The author recounts his spiritual journey: experiences of the Spirit through beauty, love, and worship, as well as reflections on how he understands the nature of the Spirit. He is especially concerned about the transcendent and immanent qualities of the Spirit, the relation of the Spirit to suffering and evil, and the significance of the creation as the incarnation of the Spirit.
Autobiography - Beauty - Evil - Holy Spirit - Love - Spiritual Journey - Spirituality - Suffering - Transcendence - Worship

333 *Walk with Me: Nonviolent Accompaniment in Guatemala*
Morton, Peg (1997) - *(eBook available)*
The author learned about the destruction in Central America being caused with the support, training, and participation of the U.S. government, and she learned of the holocaust which had taken place in Guatemala. After that Central America unveiling, way opened for her to give up her counseling career and to return to fulltime volunteer activism.
Accompaniment - Central America - Foreign Policy - Guatemala - Indigenous Peoples - International Relations - Nonviolence - Social Action - Social Concerns - War

334 *The Bosnian Student Project: A Response to Genocide*
Hostetter, C. Douglas (1997) - *(eBook available)*
The author tells, poignantly and lovingly, the story of more than 150 Bosnian students who were helped to continue their education in the U.S. through this project of the Fellowship of Reconciliation.
Bosnia - Social Concerns - Violence - War - Youth

335 *Come Aside and Rest Awhile*
Taber, Frances Irene (1997) - *(eBook available)*
Out of her own rich experience, Fran Taber expands William Penn's vision for retreats. She describes the retreat movement as a significant thread weaving together the ecumenical religious community.
Contemplation - Ecumenism - Renewal - Retreats - Spiritual Practices

336 *God's Spirit in Nature*
Brown, Judith Reynolds (1998) - *(eBook available)*
The author gives us a moving meditation on the metaphysical
sense of the Earth as the body of God. The writing was
inspired by her experiences in a 1995 Pendle Hill course,
Global Spirituality and Earth Ethics.
Ecology - Nature - Social Concerns - Spirituality

337 *There Is a Spirit: The Nayler Sonnets*
Boulding, Kenneth Ewart (1998) - *(eBook available)*
These sonnets by Kenneth Boulding were first published
nearly 50 years ago. Based on the famous last words of James
Nayler, one of the early Quakers, the author says these poems
were written to express the hope that lies beyond despair.
Hope - Nayler, James - Poetry

338 *Touched by God in Quaker Meeting*
Carroll, Kenneth Lane (1998) - *(eBook available)*
The author maintains that it is part of the spiritual experience
of Friends that we, both individually and collectively, have
found inspiration and guidance coming to us through our
meetings for worship. Drawing upon his experience and
discovery, he shares accounts of some of the meetings for
worship where Friends were truly touched by God.
Experience - Faith and Practice - God - Meeting for Worship
- Worship

339 *Prayer: Beginning Again*
Keane, Sheila (1998)
What is prayer? Petition, intercession, worship, confession, listening, meditation, a way of being, desire for God, faithful actions, gifts of grace, mystery... In an expanded definition of prayer, we must go beyond the mere saying of prayers and include these ways of being, yearning, acting, or receiving prayer. Prayer is the expression of our individual relationships with the incomprehensible and mysterious Divine Being.
Discernment - Prayer

340 *A Song of Death, Our Spiritual Birth: A Quaker Way of Dying*
McIver, Lucy Screechfield (1998) - *(eBook available)*
As a Cadbury scholar at Pendle Hill, the author researched seventeenth century and modern experiences of death and dying among Friends. She offers guidance for pastoral care in our meeting communities.
Death - Pastoral Care - Quakerism

341 *Sickness, Suffering, and Healing: More Stories from Another Place*
Gates, Thomas (1998) - *(eBook available)*
More stories from this American doctor's compassionate encounter with Kenyans in their country. The stories describe the challenges of suffering and the response of African faith.
Africa - Autobiography - Faith - Healing - Kenya - Missionaries - Service Work - Suffering

342 *Beyond the Bars: A Quaker Primer for Prison Visitors*
Maddock, Keith R. (1999) - *(eBook available)*
Written with sensitivity and grace, this essay depicts Friends'
Testimonies in prison service work. By example of listening
and respect, more than by preaching, the author has much to
say about being present in prison and receiving gifts from
people who are incarcerated.
Prison - Social Action - Testimonies

343 *Quakerism and Science*
Schwabe, Calvin W. (1999) - *(eBook available)*
A Quaker scientist affirms that science and Quakerism have
more in common than science has with other avenues of
religious expression. The wider recognition of the
commonalities could encourage both inner and outer peace.
**Continuing Revelation - Inspiration - Leadings - Peace -
Quakerism - Science**

344 *Dancing with God through the Storm: Mysticism and
Mental Illness*
Elam, Jennifer (1999) - *(eBook available)*
A Quaker psychologist challenges any absolute distinction
between experience of God and mental illness, describes the
stages of growth possible in discerning them, and asks Friends
to provide safe communities in which people are not
mislabeled. With color illustrations by the author.
Psychology - Mental Illness - Mysticism - Spirituality

345 *More than Equals: Spiritual Friendships*
Roberts, Trish (1999) - *(eBook available)*
The author advocates for this growing form of spiritual
nurture among Friends and gives good guidelines for seeking
and sustaining a spiritual friendship.
**Community - Pastoral Care - Spiritual Friendship - Spiritual
Nurture**

346 *Treasure in Clay Jars*
Sutton, Elizabeth Ostrander (1999) - *(eBook available)*
The author rediscovered a powerful sense of God calling her
to a more real spiritual life through her artistic work with clay
in the Pendle Hill studio. Photographs and devotions record
that experience.
Art and Religion - Clay - Spirituality

347 *Tall Poppies: Supporting Gifts of Ministry and Eldering in
the Monthly Meeting*
Grundy, Martha Paxson (1999) - *(eBook available)*
The pamphlet provides a description of the traditional Quaker
understanding of power and spiritual authority, and God's
gifts in relation to them, particularly gifts of ministry and
eldering. The author suggests ways that monthly meetings can
support and nurture ministry and the individual Friends
through whom it comes.
**Authority - Discipline - Doctrine - Eldering - Faith and
Practice - Gifts - Gospel Order - Ministry - Oversight -
Power - Quakerism - Traveling in the Ministry**

348 *Journey to Bosnia, Return to Self*
O'Hatnick, Suzanne Hubbard (2000) - *(eBook available)*
The author describes her call to serve as a peace activist in
Bosnia with Christian Peacemaker Teams, and then chronicles
the work she undertook, illuminating the transformative
power of her experience.
Bosnia - Christian Peacemaker Teams - Croatia -
Ecumenism - Herzegovina - Peace - Serbia - Service Work -
Spiritual Journey - War

349 *The Radiance and Risks of Mythmaking*
Kilpack, Gilbert H. (2000) - *(eBook available)*
A longtime friend of Pendle Hill offers vignettes that shine
with the Presence and challenge the conventional boundaries
among literature, theology, and personal narrative.
Autobiography - Civilian Public Service - Education -
Literature - Mythology - Theology - World War II

350 *I Have Always Wanted to be Jewish: And Now, Thanks
to the Religious Society of Friends, I Am*
Gorfinkel, Claire (2000) - *(eBook available)*
The author, a Quaker and a Jew, shares how the intersection
of these two spiritual traditions has strengthened her identity
as a Jew, deepened her faith, and intensified her witness with
Quakers.
Community - Conversion - Convincement - Judaism -
Politics - Religious Life - Spiritual Journey

351 *Jacob Boehme: Insights into the Challenge of Evil*
Liem, Ann (2000) - *(eBook available)*
A Quaker examines what constitutes evil in our modern era,
drawing on the theological work of the 16th century German
mystic, Jacob Boehme. This is a reprint of pamphlet #214 with
a preface by Larry Ingle.
Boehme, Jacob - Evil - Good - Mysticism - Christianity -
Theology

352 *Navigating the Living Waters of the Gospel of John: On
Wading with Children and Swimming with Elephants*
Anderson, Paul N. (2000) - *(eBook available)*
A Quaker theologian introduces major themes in the Gospel
of John for newcomers to the Bible as well as for serious
biblical scholars.
Belief - Bible - Gospel of John - Jesus

353 *Letting That Go, Keeping This: The Spiritual Pilgrimage
of Fritz Eichenberg*
Harnden, Philip (2001) - *(eBook available)*
Fritz Eichenberg, internationally known woodcut artist, has
inspired a generation of Quakers and Catholics in their social
witness. This author eloquently elucidates five important
inspirations for the artist: animals, Lao-Tzu, Russian novelists,
Quakers, and the Catholic Worker. With illustrations by Fritz
Eichenberg.
Art and Religion - Biography - Catholic Worker -
Convincement - Day, Dorothy - Eichenberg, Fritz - Faith -
Wood Engraving - Skepticism - Spiritual Journey

354 *Live the Questions: Write into the Answers*
Parsons, Barbara E. and Mary Chase Morrison (2001) - *(eBook available)*
Two consummate journal writers describe the writing process and give exercises for keeping a journal.
Journaling - Reflection - Spiritual Practices - Writing

355 *In Beauty: A Quaker Approach to End-of-Life Care*
Backstrom, Kirsten (2001) - *(eBook available)*
This author shares the story of experiences in her monthly meeting to illustrate how our dying can be as fully centered in God as our living.
Beauty - Cancer - Death - Hospice Care - Integrity - Listening - Simplicity - Wholeness

356 *Testimony: John Woolman on Today's Global Economy*
Morse, David E. (2001) - *(eBook available)*
What would John Woolman do in the face of the current injustices brought on by globalization? This pamphlet provides a creative and provocative response.
Economics - Globalization - Slavery - Social Action - Testimonies - Truth - Woolman, John - World Politics

357 *A Plea for the Poor*
Woolman, John (2001)
This early Quaker minister's essay relates poverty to wasteful consumption, brings the rich and powerful to account, and calls for simplicity as a style of life. With an introduction by Phillips P. Moulton.
Ethics - Morality - Poverty - Reparations - Simplicity - Slavery - Wealth - Woolman, John

358 *Reflections from a Prayer Vigil for Peace*
Gallery, John Andrew (2001)
The author shares reflections born of his participation in an extended prayer vigil for peace. It includes thoughts on sowing peace, faithfulness, and prayer.
Demonstrations - Faith - Peace - Prayer - Social Action - Social Concerns - Vigils

359 *The Existential Theology of Nikos Kazantkakis*
Dossor, Howard F. (2002) - *(eBook available)*
The author finds that Kazantzakis's theology gives us insight on how to live fully, joyfully, and faithfully.
Atheism - Existentialism - God - Kazantzakis, Nikos - Literature - Theology

360 *Quaker Social Testimony in our Personal and Corporate Life*
Dale, Jonathan (2002) - *(eBook available)*
Lifestyle and politics are integral expressions of what human beings are meant to be: loving, truthful, peaceful, and centered on God.
Community - Economics - Fair Trade - Food - Honesty - Integrity - Organizing - Politics - Simplicity - Testimonies - Social Concerns

361 *Journey through Skepticism*
Warren, Roland Leslie (2002) - *(eBook available)*
In this pamphlet, the author describes how he has come to live in the certainty of a spirit that unites him to something beyond himself.
Agnosticism - Atheism - Belief - Christianity - Skepticism - Spiritual Journey

362 *Bringing God Home: Exploring Family Spirituality*
Rehard, Mary Kay (2002) - *(eBook available)*
The communities of L'Arche and Taizé have influenced the
author's insights and practices. Both encourage healthy family
environments and the nurture of children's spirituality. "Let
the little children come to me, and do not stop them: for it is
to such as these that the kingdom of heaven belongs." -
Matthew 19:14.
Children - Community - Education - Family Life - Parenting
- Spirituality

363 *Profession and Practice: Quaker Perspectives on Healing
as Ministry*
Flannery, Maureen A. (2002) - *(eBook available)*
This pamphlet invites Quaker professionals, healers, and
nurturers to a way of practicing professionalism that both
reclaims the wisdom in our Quaker tradition and affirms what
is of value in alternative secular models.
Healing - Leadings - Ministry - Quakerism - Work

364 *Gift of Days: Report on an Illness*
Morrison, Mary Chase (2003) - *(eBook available)*
In this moving pamphlet the author writes: "Maybe this is the
death I was desiring so intensely during my illness—this death
of the separate spinning mind as it merges into the intense life
of the present moment. If so, then Yes, there's more. Much
more... My work is to be ready to receive it when it comes as I
would a visit from an old friend."
Death - Illness

365 *The Authority of Our Meetings is the Power of God*
Lacey, Paul A. (2003) - *(eBook available)*
The author sees Quakers at a crossroads in dealing with issues
of authority and power in church governance and offers some
assessment of the costs of traveling one way or another. He
challenges Friends to find their balance between tolerance of
diversity and corporate unity.
**Authority - Discipline - Diversity - Faith and Practice -
Gospel Order - Governance - Meeting for Business - Power
- Quaker Process - Religious Society of Friends - Unity**

366 *Invitation to a Deeper Communion*
Martin, Marcelle (2003) - *(eBook available)*
This pamphlet examines what it was about the belief and
practice of early Friends that invited direct experience of the
Spirit. It also describes explorations by contemporary Friends
to seek a deeper communion with God in worship, suggesting
that a renewal of worship will help Friends today become
powerful witnesses to another way of life.
**Communion - Early Friends - Faith and Practice - Holy
Spirit - Leadings - Renewal - Worship**

367 *Quaker in Vietnam: Rick Thompson*
Taylor, Beth (2003)
This pamphlet is a personal history of Rick Thompson, who
worked for the American Friends Service Committee in
Vietnam during the war, and who is one of the few Quakers
to have died there. The author uncovers his journey of
conscience as it led to pacifism and then compelled him to
help in relief efforts in Vietnam during the war.
**American Friends Service Committee - Biography -
Conscientious Objection - Pacifism - Peace - Vietnam -
Service Work**

368 *On Retiring to Kendal (and Beyond): A Literary Excursion*
Bien, Peter (2003) - *(eBook available)*
The author employs poetry and literature to reflect on the meaning of retirement and whether death is an unmitigated calamity. He concludes it is not better to live forever, and that strangely, death enhances life, rather than negating it.
Aging - Death - Literature - Poetry - Retirement

369 *Meditations on the Prayer of St. Francis*
Curo, Anne (2003) - *(eBook available)*
Starting with the metaphor of the self as a musical instrument on which God performs, the author reflects on the beloved prayer of St. Francis as instructions for a life of Christian peacemaking. She uses examples from her experiences in homeless activism and her study of various faith traditions to explore the wisdom in the prayer line by line.
Peace - Prayer - Social Action - St. Francis

370 *A Quaker in the Zendo*
Smith, Steve (2004) - *(eBook available)*
In this pamphlet the author tells the story of his journey through Zen to a rediscovery of directions for spiritual formation practiced by the earliest Quakers.
Buddhism - Christianity - Quakerism - Zen

371 *Members One of Another: The Dynamics of Membership in Quaker Meeting*
Gates, Thomas (2004) - *(eBook available)*
In Quaker faith and practice, the individual and the meeting are in a dynamic, mutually supportive, and reciprocal relation. In this essay Tom Gates examines many of the factors affecting the relationship between the Seeker and the Meeting, before and during membership.
Faith and Practice - Membership - Quakerism

372 *Living the Peace Testimony: The Legacy of Howard and Anna Brinton*
Manousos, Anthony (2004) - *(eBook available)*
Born of Quaker families, Howard Brinton and Anna Cox Brinton met doing Friends relief work in Germany after World War I and devoted their lives together to nurturing Quakerism, social activism, peacemaking, and peacemakers from coast to coast in the United States and, in their last years, in Asia.
Biography - Brinton, Anna and Howard - Peace - Pendle Hill - Testimonies

373 *Group Spiritual Nurture: The Wisdom of Spiritual Listening*
Clement, Daphne (2004) - *(eBook available)*
This essay by Daphne Clement, an experienced facilitator of Spiritual Nurture Groups, is both an introduction to spiritual nurture and a guide for those interested in creating a Spiritual Nurture Group.
Listening - Pastoral Care - Spiritual Nurture - Worship

374 *The Practice of the Love of God*
Boulding, Kenneth Ewart (2004) - *(eBook available)*
The author urges us to explore love unlimited by time or
place—love in our families, with our neighbors, and in our
meetings and churches, all possible through our love for God.
He concludes with his vision for the world and his assurance
that there is no room for despair, that God is always
redeeming the world. With an introduction by Elise Boulding.
Family Life - God - Love

375 *Quaker Views on Mysticism*
Abbott, Margery Post (2004) - *(eBook available)*
This pamphlet considers how Friends today recognize and
respond to the guidance of the Inward Light of Christ. It
describes varying Quaker views on mysticism and the mystical,
touching upon the need to continually test leadings in the
silence of Quaker worship and in the arms of Quaker
community.
Community - Inward Light - Leadings - Mysticism -
Religious Society of Friends - Worship

376 *Henry J. Cadbury: Scholar, Activist, Disciple*
Bacon, Margaret Hope (2005) - *(eBook available)*
Henry Joel Cadbury was widely acknowledged as an author
and as a biblical scholar and translator of the highest order; a
professor who challenged students' thinking in the halls of
Harvard Divinity School, Haverford, and Bryn Mawr Colleges,
as well as at Pendle Hill; and the consummate Quaker activist.
Cadbury, Henry Joel - Biography

377 *Creeds and Quakers: What's Belief Got to Do with It?*
Griswold, Robert (2005) – *(eBook available)*
Quaker spiritual authority lies not in belief systems and in
creeds, but in the direct communion between individuals and
the Divine Spirit. The pamphlet's author asserts that Friends
too often hold Quaker testimonies as ideals, as ends in
themselves, rather than as fruits of the Spirit. Without
spiritual grounding, testimonies become creeds.
Authority – Belief – Creeds – Faith and Practice – History –
Quakerism – Testimonies – Theology

378 *Living in Virtue, Declaring against War*
Smith, Steve (2005) – *(eBook available)*
Born in an era of profound spiritual awakening, the Quaker
Peace Testimony remains a radical challenge today—to live
Jesus's message of love, forgiveness, and reconciliation. This is
the story of the author's discovery and conviction in the Light.
Convincement – Peace – Spiritual Journey – Spirituality –
Testimonies – Violence

379 *Living Truth: A Spiritual Portrait of Pierre Ceresole*
Maddock, Keith R. (2005) – *(eBook available)*
The author paints a portrait of the spiritual growth of a
passionate, poetic, solitary seeker of Truth who urges us to set
aside our theories and our fears and instead take up the tools
that are needed to create a more humane, just, and peaceful
world.
Biography – Ceresole, Pierre – Civilian Public Service –
Peace – Service Work

380 *A Very Good Week Behind Bars*
Ravndal, Janeal Turnbull (2005) – *(eBook available)*
The author writes of her week in Philadelphia's Federal
Detention Center after she chose to ignore orders not to block
entry to a courthouse as the U.S. began to attack Iraq early in
2003.
Civil Disobedience – Prayer – Prison – Social Action – War

381 *Fire of the Heart: Norman Morrison's Legacy in Viet
Nam and at Home*
Welsh, Anne Morrison (2005) – *(eBook available)*
The author tells the moving story of her husband's self-
sacrifice at the Pentagon in November 1965 in a desperate
effort to help end a war he abhorred. In telling her husban"s
story, the author also shares her own spiritual journey of
forgiveness, acceptance, and gradual recovery from life's
wounds.
Death – Forgiveness – Pacifism – Peace – Vietnam –
Spiritual Journey – War

382 *Holding One Another in the Light*
Martin, Marcelle (2006) – *(eBook available)*
The author offers a personal account of her discovery of and
experiences with intercessory prayer. She describes the many
forms it takes among Friends today, from interpersonal prayer
support, to meetings for healing, to a prayerful witness for
peace on earth.
Healing – Holding in the Light – Peace – Prayer –
Spirituality

383 *Answering the Call to Heal the World*
Schenck, Patience A. (2006) – *(eBook available)*
The author walks us through the life of a leading: hearing a
call, testing our discernment, overcoming the obstacles to
faithfulness, finding the support we need, and, finally,
recognizing when our work is done.
Discernment – Gifts – Healing – Leadings – Social Concerns

384 *The Mystery of Quaker Light*
Bien, Peter (2006) – *(eBook available)*
What has Light meant to different people throughout the
ages? How did various ideas about Light influence the
prologue to John's Gospel? What did early Friends understand
Light to mean? In this pamphlet, the author explores the
theology and poetry of Friends' favorite religious symbol.
**Bible – Early Friends – Gospel of John – History – Inward
Light – Logos – Theology**

385 *In God We Die*
Ostrom, Warren (2006) – *(eBook available)*
The author, who has worked closely with the aging and dying
for over two decades, offers his deeply-considered insights on
the end of life, as well as his reflections on the role of
spirituality in how we face death, and guidance for finding
clarity in our choices about our own final path.
Death – Aging – Spirituality

386 *The Mindful Quaker: A Brief Introduction to Buddhist Wisdom for Friends*
Brown, Valerie (2006) – *(eBook available)*
The author, who is both a Quaker and a Buddhist, explores the gifts that Buddhism has to offer Friends in our search for unity with the Divine Ground, for clarity in our worship, and for equanimity in our lives.
Buddhism – Meditation – Mindfulness – Peace of Mind – Quakerism – Spiritual Practices – Worship

387 *Turnaround: Growing a Twenty-First Century Religious Society of Friends*
Lloyd, Benjamin (2006) – *(eBook available)*
In this essay the author presents his own creative ideas and encouragement for a reinvigoration of our meeting communities. Which of our traditions and practices should we renew? And where are the places where continuing revelation calls us to be open to the winds of change that will come with the next generation of Quaker leaders?
Community – Continuing Revalation – Leadership – Meetings – Religious Life – Religious Society of Friends – Renewal

388 *Expectant Listening: Finding God's Thread of Guidance*
Wajda, Michael (2007) – *(eBook available)*
Out of a great hunger for God's love and guidance, the author has spent his adult life seeking to experience the presence of God. In this pamphlet, he offers readers his personal story and tells what he has learned about the practice of expectant listening.
Discernment – God – Listening – Spiritual Journey – Spiritual Practices – Worship

389 *From West Point to Quakerism*
Heller, Mike (2007) – *(eBook available)*
The author reflects on his painful and sometimes lonely
passage and on how way opened for him to discover himself
and his place in the world.
Autobiography – Religious Life – Spiritual Journey

390 *Special Education as a Spiritual Journey*
Resman, Michael (2007) – *(eBook available)*
The author, who works in special education as an
occupational therapist, has had much occasion to grapple with
difficult questions. The answers he found for himself come
not from church teachings, nor from his own reasonings, but
from mystical insight, or as early Friends would say, from
spiritual openings.
**Disabilities – Education – Mysticism – Suffering – Special
Education – Spirituality**

391 *Getting Rooted: Living in the Cross, A Path to Joy and
Liberation*
Drayton, Brian (2007) – *(eBook available)*
The author explores the idea of rootedness at multiple levels
in order to reveal the ways in which we may derive the most
nourishment from the roots that we seek to rediscover so that
God's Spirit may flourish within us and through us.
Quakerism – Spirituality – Theology

392 *Spirit-Led Eldering: Integral to Our Faith and Practice*
Larrabee, Margery Mears (2007) – *(eBook available)*
The author and other Friends are urging us to rediscover
eldering as a valuable practice that can nurture the spiritual
lives of individual Friends and of Friends' meetings. Decades
of experience, wisdom, and deep reflection are contained in
these pages.
Doctrine – Eldering – Faith and Practice – Spiritual Nurture

393 *Rebecca Janney Timbres Clark: Turned in the Hand of
God*
Back, Lyndon S. (2007) – *(eBook available)*
Rebecca Janney Timbres Clark led a remarkable life that
spanned all of the twentieth century. This pamphlet explores
one year in that life, the year when a young, sheltered Quaker
from Baltimore took the first steps toward a career of service
that would take her around the world.
American Friends Service Committee – Biography – Clark,
Rebecca Janney Timbres – Service Work

394 *God's Healing Grace: Reflections on a Journey with
Mental and Spiritual Illness*
Gilpin, Mariellen (2008) – *(eBook available)*
The author's story provides a model of someone whose
experienced reality is not commonly shared, but who has
grown as a person and as a Quaker in close relationship with
her Friends meeting. The voices of persons labeled with
mental illnesses are voices in our communities that need to be
heard.
Healing – Mental Illness – Spiritual Journey

395 *Walt Whitman's Spiritual Epic*
Robertson, Michael (2008) – *(eBook available)*
With particular attention to the perspectives of Friends, the author walks the reader through *Song of Myself*, noting its beauties, its challenges, and its deep inspiration.
Literature – Poetry – Spirituality – Whitman, Walt

396 *God Raising Us: Parenting as a Spiritual Practice*
Flanagan, Eileen (2008) – *(eBook available)*
In telling her own story—the challenges faced, the lessons learned—the author calls on Friends to recognize parenthood as a phase of spiritual development with special gifts and needs, and suggests ways that we may begin to support the faith lives of parents and help our meetings be more fully multigenerational.
Children – Family Life – Parenting – Spiritual Practices – Spirituality

397 *Quaker Witness as Sacrament*
Snyder, Daniel O. (2008) – *(eBook available)*
The author has spent his adult years wrestling with the apparent dichotomy between the pull of an inward call to a spiritual life of contemplation and an outward call to respond to the problems of the world. He has concluded that rather than competing with each other, these two calls are parts of a single whole that must be joined if he is to be faithful to either.
Contemplation – Prayer – Sacraments – Social Action – Spirituality – Witness

398 *The Messenger That Goes Before: Reading Margaret Fell for Spiritual Nurture*
Birkel, Michael (2008) – *(eBook available)*
The author has discovered in the letters of Margaret Fell, one of the founding members of the Religious Society of Friends, a treasure trove of wise and loving counsel for those on the spiritual journey.
Biography – Fell, Margaret – History – Spiritual Nurture

399 *Matthew 18: Wisdom for Living in Community*
Green, Connie McPeak and Marty Paxson Grundy (2008) – *(eBook available)*
The authors have spent years exploring the eighteenth chapter of the Gospel of Matthew, which contains Jesus's advice to his disciples about how to get along with one another. In this essay, they describe what they have learned from their efforts to be faithful.
Bible – Community – Conflict Resolution – Gospels – Human Relations

400 *Finding the Taproot of Simplicity: A Movement between Inner Knowledge and Outer Action*
Taber, Frances Irene (2009) – *(eBook available)*
This essay explores the spiritual basis of Friends' testimony of simplicity: how it evolved from the efforts of early Friends to live in a way that fostered the spiritual richness of their lives, and how it continues to speak today in the lives of those who seek to find not merely balance, but an unseamed wholeness of their inward and outward journeys.
Integrity – Simplicity – Testimonies – Wholeness

401 *Three Ravens and Two Widows*
Kelly, Richard Macy (2009) – *(eBook available)*
Using the metaphor of the ancient ballad "The Three
Ravens," the author invites us to explore how history and
family traditions may limit our understanding of Truth or give
us the strength and vision to see new possibilities in times
when disagreements trouble our communities.
**Biography – Community – Conflict Resolution – Family Life
– History**

402 *Christianity and the Inner Life: Twenty-First Century
Reflections on the Words of Early Friends*
Abbott, Margery Post (2009) – *(eBook available)*
In her explorations of the writings of early Friends, the author
has discovered her own approach to Christian perspectives,
one that speaks specifically to her experiences of the Divine
Light. She finds inspiration and fellowship with early and
modern Friends for whom Christ is central, without excluding
the inspiration of other religious traditions.
**Christian Life – Christianity – Early Friends – Inward Light –
Quakerism – Spirituality**

403 *Integrity, Ecology, and Community: The Motion of Love*
Ratcliffe, Jennie M. (2009) – *(eBook available)*
Drawing on her years of experience and reflection as a
scientist and active participant in peace and ecological
concerns, the author believes that a deeper transformation is
needed. A spiritual awareness of our oneness reminds us that
we live in intimate relationship and kinship with each other,
the earth, and the Divine.
**Community – Ecology – Integrity – Love – Nature –
Nonviolence – Reconciliation – Simplicity – Spirituality**

404 *Kindling a Life of Concern: Spirit-Led Quaker Action*
Kirk, Jack (2009) – *(eBook available)*
The author discusses how concerns arise and are opened to us,
how we may test them, and how we may find in them a center
of spiritual gravity for our lives. How do we discover our
callings as individuals, and what is our calling as a community
of Friends?

Concerns – Community – Discernment – Ecology –
Leadings – Social Action

405 *Envisioning a Moral Economy*
Head, Tom (2010) – *(eBook available)*
A Quaker economist explores how we might think about our
economy and its purposes in new ways by including religious
sources of wisdom and morality in our vision of a just and
humane economic future.

Economics – Morality

406 *The Mind of Christ: Bill Taber on Meeting for Business*
Taber, William P. and Michael Birkel (2010) – *(eBook available)*
Bill Taber addressed the rewards and challenges of Quaker
business process in a number of presentations to Friends
groups. Michael Birkel has edited Bill's notes for these talks
into an essay on how Friends can carry into business meeting
the practices and attitudes that open the way to Spirit-led
decisions in our communities.

Clearness – Discernment – Doctrine – Meeting for Business
– Quaker Process – Right Order – Taber, Bill – Unity

407 *Living from the Center: Mindfulness Meditation and Centering for Friends*
Brown, Valerie (2010) – *(eBook available)*
The author, a teacher of centering practices, a Buddhist, and an active Friend, draws upon her experience and study to describe for Friends how these various traditions can offer us a better understanding and preparedness for our precious, elusive, mysterious, and simple practice of centering into worship.
Buddhism – Centering – Meditation – Mindfulness – Spiritual Practices – Worship

408 *An Art of Small Resurrections: Surviving the Texas Death Chamber*
Long, Walter (2010) – *(eBook available)*
A defense attorney for Texas death row inmates wrestles with the apparent contradiction between the teachings of Jesus and widespread tolerance for government violence in a state where most citizens identify themselves as Christian.
Christianity – Death Penalty – Jesus – Justice – Prison – Violence

409 *"Who Do You Say I Am?"*
Wilson, Lloyd Lee (2010) – *(eBook available)*
This pamphlet invites readers to meet Jesus as the author has come to know Him and to further explore for themselves, "Who do you say I am?"
Christianity – Jesus – Quakerism

410 *Confident Quakerism*
Dandelion, Ben Pink (2010) – *(eBook available)*
After a personal crisis shook his confidence in himself, the
author considered seriously the spiritual meaning of
"confidence" (literally, to live and act "with faith"). His
insights are especially meaningful for liberal Friends,
individually and as a society, as we look toward the future.
Community – Quakerism – Religious Life – Religious
Society of Friends – Renewal – Spirituality

411 *Plow up the Fallow Ground: A Meditation in the
Company of Early Friends*
Harper, Lu (2011) – *(eBook available)*
Through this extended exploration, and by offering rich
queries for personal meditation, the author invites readers to
rediscover a Quaker way of deriving powerful, personal
meaning from the Bible.
Bible – Early Friends – Parables – Queries

412 *Answering the Violence: Encounters with Perpetrators*
Lampen, John (2011) – *(eBook available)*
The author, who has served as a Quaker peace worker in
Northern Ireland and elsewhere, draws on his own
experiences and the accounts of other peace workers to
explore the controversies, risks, rewards, and possible benefits
of reaching out in friendship to perpetrators of violence.
Peace – Nonviolence – Northern Ireland – Violence –
Witness

413 *James Nayler Speaking*
Drayton, Brian (2011) - *(eBook available)*
The author found in the writings of this influential and controversial Friend messages that speak to the turmoil of our times, just as they spoke to the turmoil of 1650s England. Some central themes in the ministry of James Nayler are explored, with attention to how they address the most basic challenges of faithfulness in what early Friends called "the Lamb's War."
Early Friends – History – Nayler, James – Religious Society of Friends – Spirituality – Theology

414 *Seeking Inner Peace: Presence, Pain, and Wholeness*
De Sa, Elizabeth (2011) - *(eBook available)*
The author describes her own quest for a life of spiritual authenticity and inner peace in an essay that probes deeply into the lessons learned and the rewards reaped in a search for union with the Divine. In meditation practice she peels back the layers of pain arising from unhealed wounds and false expectations of herself, obstacles that stand in the way of full acceptance of self, others, and the Divine.
Authenticity – Healing – Inner Peace – Meditation – Peace – Presence – Spiritual Journey – Spirituality – Suffering – Wholeness

415 *Living Our Testimony on Equality: A White Friend's Experience*
Schenck, Patience A. (2011) – *(eBook available)*
The principle of human equality is a testimony that Friends are both proud of and challenged by. Proclaiming the importance of equality among peoples is far easier than living equality, day to day and interpersonally. The author has dedicated years of study, self-examination, and experimentation to living racial equality in a society that still supports inequality in its institutions.
Equality – Race Relations – Social Concerns – Testimonies

416 *Grief, Forgiveness, and Redemption as a Way of Transformation*
Pryce, Elaine (2012) – *(eBook available)*
The traumatic loss of a loved one is among the most devastating hurdles that life can throw in a person's path. Drawing from her own experience, as well as from art, literature, and traditional wisdom, the author explores the spiritual aspects of grief, recovery from grief, forgiveness, and the blessings of acceptance.
Death – Forgiveness – Grief – Spirituality – Suffering – Transformation

417 *John Yungblut: Passing the Mystical Torch*
Finn, Charles C. (2012) – *(eBook available)*
In this pamphlet the author unveils the faith and vision of
John Yungblut. At the heart of this story, readers will discover
a spiritual "genealogy": Rufus Jones, Pierre Teilhard de
Chardin, and Carl Jung influenced John Yungblut, who
became a spiritual guide and friend to Charlie Finn.
Biography – Christianity – Evolution – Jones, Rufus – Jung
– Mysticism – Teilhard de Chardin, Pierre – Theology –
Yungblut, John

418 *Some Thoughts on Becoming Eighty-Five*
Shetter, William Z. (2012) – *(eBook available)*
The experience of long life and spiritual fruits of aging are the
focus of this meditative walk through eighty-five years of the
author's life experience: among Friends, in relationship, as an
ongoing seeker and keen observer of the world.
Aging – Autobiography – Community – Death – Family Life
– Spiritual Journey – Spirituality

419 *Nurturing Children's Spiritual Well-Being*
Crompton, Margaret (2012) – *(eBook available)*
The author focuses on communication between children and
adults in Quaker families and meetings. She includes practical
advice along with stories that reveal children's innate
spirituality.
Children – Communication – Education – Family Life –
Parenting – Religious Education – Spirituality

420 *Waging Peace: Discipline and Practice*
Haines, Pamela (2012) – *(eBook available)*
The author offers readers ways to become "nonviolent warriors" through practices that show us how to hope, grieve, listen, welcome conflict, mend, speak truth, and cultivate courage.
Conflict Resolution – Discipline – Nonviolence – Peace – Social Action – Spiritual Practices

421 *Heartfulness: Renewing Heart, Mind, and Spirit on Retreat and Beyond*
Brown, Valerie (2013) – *(eBook available)*
The author guides readers toward renewal of mind, heart, and spirit by encouraging them to take time away from the busyness of their lives through retreat. She encourages the "big questions"—What has meaning and purpose in my life? What am I avoiding? What brings me most alive?—and offers specific practices for retreatants to cultivate in everyday life.
Contemplation – Renewal – Retreats – Spiritual Practices – Spirituality

422 *Reclaiming the Transcendent: God in Process*
Gates, Thomas (2013) – *(eBook available)*
God is commonly imagined as a supreme Being, acting from afar to influence events in the world. For many people today, this image of God has become unbelievable. The author presents process theology as another way of understanding God that is more congruent with a scientific worldview, as well as with the biblical witness and with the understanding of early Friends.
God – Paradox – Process Theology – Theology – Transcendence

423 *Queries as Prayers*
Rembert, Ron B. (2013) – *(eBook available)*
As a participant in an ecumenical workshop where he was the
only Quaker, the author found himself experimenting with
new uses for the traditional Quaker practice of responding to
queries. In adapting new practices to a Quaker sensibility, he
finds new ways of using queries and explores the significance
of writing our prayers.
Prayer – Queries – Spiritual Practices – Writing

424 *Nonviolent Direct Action as a Spiritual Path*
Taylor, Richard K. (2013) – *(eBook available)*
A lifelong nonviolent activist has observed that spiritual
openings and deep faith experiences in his life have often
occurred in the midst of an action. Using his own stories,
which span the civil rights movement to the present time,
Taylor explores the relationship between spirituality and
nonviolent direct action.
**Nonviolence – Social Action – Spiritual Journey –
Spirituality**

425 *The Light Within: Then and Now*
Ambler, Rex (2013) – *(eBook available)*
When contemporary Friends speak to each other of the Light
Within, do we have a shared understanding of what we mean?
Is it the same Light that George Fox spoke of? How could we
be enriched—as individuals and as a community—by recovering
some of the early Quaker experiences of Light?
**Early Friends – History – Inward Light – Spiritual Practices
– Theology**

426 *'But Who Do You Say That I Am?': Quakers and Christ Today*

Gwyn, Douglas (2014) – *(eBook available)*

The author explores the different stances Quakers have assumed in relation to Christianity, from the unique "primitive Christianity revived" of early Friends, through the foundationist, Conservative, ecumenical, interfaith, universalist, and nontheist positions of different Quakers today.

Christianity – Early Friends – Ecumenism – Jesus – Nontheism – Quakerism – Theology – Universalism

427 *Radical Hospitality*

Wilson, Lloyd Lee (2014) – *(eBook available)*

Hospitality is both a way of living in the Kingdom of God in the present moment and a way of bringing the Kingdom into its fullness for everyone, making the Kingdom complete both now and everywhere. It is radical hospitality because it stems from the very root of our relationship with God. To practice radical hospitality is to be in the world as God is in the world.

Christianity – Community – God – Hospitality – Kingdom of God – Social Action

428 *Spiritual Accompaniment: An Experience of Two Friends Traveling in the Ministry*
Walling, Cathy and Elaine Emily (2014) – *(eBook available)*
As the practice of spiritual accompaniment—or eldering—undergoes a resurgence among Friends, two such companions give us an account of eldering from the viewpoint of the companion and the minister she traveled with. This jointly-written account explores the lessons, challenges, and gifts of that experience.
Accompaniment – Eldering – Faith and Practice – Ministry – Traveling in the Ministry

429 *What We Stand On*
Christiansen, Paul (2014) – *(eBook available)*
The author calls Quakers to account for how well we face the seeds of war within our own lives. His strong condemnation of our tendency to rest too much in the comfort of our First World privileges is answered by his inspiring message about why we should have hope and courage as a people who can light the way to peace in our world.
Peace – Privilege – Religious Life – Testimonies – War

430 *The Door In*
Crauder, Renee (2014) – *(eBook available)*
The author, a spiritual director and leader of workshops and retreats on the spiritual life, describes her own journey, a decades-long search for a deeper relationship with the Divine. Her inspiring account describes her path—a combination of Quaker and Jesuit practices—and the discoveries and gifts of the Spirit she has encountered along the way.
Prayer – Spiritual Journey – Spirituality

431 *Revelation and Revolution: Answering the Call to Radical Faithfulness*
Chase, Steve (2015) – *(eBook available)*
For the author, being a faithful friend and follower of Jesus has always meant being engaged in nonviolent revolutionary work to bring about a beloved community which embodies spiritual wisdom, social justice, and ecological sustainability. His understanding of this call is informed by the Jewish prophets, Jesus, early Quakers, and the life example of Martin Luther King, Jr.
Community – Continuing Revelation – Faithfulness – Jesus – Leadings – King, Martin Luther – Nonviolence – Revolution – Social Action – Social Concerns – Witness

432 *A Death Chosen, A Life Given*
Russell, Hannah (2015) – *(eBook available)*
How does one find meaning and healing following the suicide of a loved one? The author, whose terminally-ill husband ended his own life, offers insights gleaned from her own journey.
Death – Grief – Suffering – Suicide

433 *Recovering Sacred Presence in a Disenchanted World*
Coelho, Mary Conrow (2015) – *(eBook available)*
Contemporary Westerners are caught between contradictory ways of understanding the world: science and faith are seemingly incompatible. And when we experience spiritual openings, when the Presence breaks through into our lives, what do we make of it?
Presence – Science – Theology

434 *A Quietness Within: The Quiet Way as Faith and*
Spirituality
Pryce, Elaine (2015) – *(eBook available)*
Drawing on the wisdom of Christian mystics, early Quakers,
and other spiritual explorers, the author contemplates the
tradition of silent inward attentiveness to Mystery and
Presence as a way to spiritual renewal, healing, and discovery.
Contemplation – Faith – Healing – Mysticism – Renewal –
Silence – Spiritual Practices

435 *"You Are My Witnesses": Witness and Testimony in the*
Biblical and Quaker Traditions
Gates, Thomas (2015) – *(eBook available)*
The experiences of the captive Hebrews in Isaiah, and of early
Friends, offer insights for modern Quakers on how to live in
faithful witness to the Light.
Bible – Early Friends – Inward Light – Quakerism –
Testimonies – Witness

436 *Spreading the Fire: Challenging and Encouraging Friends*
through Travel in the Ministry
Humphries, Debbie (2015) – *(eBook available)*
A present-day Friend called to travel in the ministry describes
her preparation to serve the call faithfully as well as what she
has learned in this service.
Faithfulness – Leadings – Traveling in the Ministry

437 *Metaphors of Meaning*
Wilson, Linda (2016) – *(eBook available)*
The author explores metaphors that are commonly used for
expressing life in the Spirit, and offers an example to readers
for finding and working with one's own metaphors.
Metaphors – Spirituality

438 *A Seal upon the Heart: Quaker Readings in the Song of
Songs*
Birkel, Michael (2016) – *(eBook available)*
A celebration of the poetry of love and the allegory of spiritual
intimacy in the Song of Songs, exploring early Friends' use of
its imagery to express their longing for union with the Divine
Spirit.
Bible – Early Friends – Love – Song of Songs

439 *Marking the Quaker Path: Seven Key Words Plus One*
Griswold, Robert (2016) – *(eBook available)*
The life of a Quaker as a series of passages: understanding
one's spiritual condition, attention to inward experience,
spiritual covenant, discipline, the practice of discernment,
spiritual authority, and beloved community.
Quakerism – Religious Life – Spiritual Journey – Spirituality

440 *Enlarging Our Circle of Love*
Fisher, Margaret (2016) – *(eBook available)*
A vegan explores the practical and spiritual challenges and
growth that arose out of following her leading to re-examine
her relationship with animal life.
Food – Leadings – Love – Testimonies – Veganism

441 *Making a Portrait of Jesus*
Lampen, John (2016) – *(eBook available)*
The author sifts through the evidence to determine what is most likely to be true about the historical Jesus.
History – Jesus

442 *Meeting at the Center: Living Love and Reconciling One with Another*
Birchard, Bruce (2016) – *(eBook available)*
An examination of the work of reconciliation in the life of the author at the personal, religious, and international levels.
Forgiveness – Love – Reconciliation

443 *Individual Spiritual Discernment: Receiving, Testing, and Implementing Leadings from a Higher Power*
Knutson, Jerry (2017) – *(eBook available)*
A how-to of methods for receiving individual spiritual guidance, testing the guidance, and then implementing it.
Discernment – Leadings – Spiritual Practices

444 *The Gathered Meeting*
Davison, Steven (2017)
The author lifts up the gathered meeting for worship as the essence of the Quaker way, and describes what fosters the gathered meeting.
Faith and Practice – Meeting for Worship – Quakerism – Worship

448 *The Inner Guide Versus the Inner Critic: The Journey from Judgment to Love*
Wolff, Christine (2017) – *(eBook available)*
A psychologist offers insight on the difference between the promptings of an "Inner Guide" whose leadings carry us forward in our spiritual growth, and an "inner critic" whose voice may confuse and disrupt our discernment.
Discernment – Psychology – Spirituality

449 *The Ecology of Quaker Meeting*
Hood, James W. (2018) – *(eBook available)*
A poetic and thoughtful meditation celebrating the deep interrelationships at work in a meeting for worship, and urging us to restore our interconnectedness with nature so we can find our way back into connectedness with a planet we have largely forgotten and abandoned.
Ecology – Nature – Meeting for Worship – Worship

450 *Money and Soul*
Haines, Pamela (2018)
Exploring our troubled relationship with money and the economic system in which we are all entangled, the author invites Friends to attend to how individual conscience and Quaker values can create a healthy and sustainable economy that provides for the common welfare.
Capitalism – Economics – Money – Social Concerns – Testimonies – Values

451 *Humanity in the Face of Inhumanity*
Williams, Sue (2018)
A collection of stories, drawing on the author's work in international conflict transformation, illustrating examples of extraordinary humanity even in extraordinarily difficult circumstances.
Conflict Resolution – Human Relations – Humanity – Values

452 *Art as Soul's Sanctuary: Meditations on Arts and Spirituality among Quakers and Beyond*
Elam, Jennifer (2018)
Art can make the transcendent and mystical manifest. Creativity can be a vehicle for connection with the Creator and with fellow humans. The author shares stories from a spiritual journey with art and creativity. With color illustrations by the author.
Art and Religion – Clay – Creativity – Mysticism – Pendle Hill – Spiritual Journey

453 *A Practical Mysticism: How Quaker Process Opens Us to the Promptings of the Divine*
Meyer, Elizabeth (2018)
Quaker business process is a group practical mysticism that opens the worshiping body to the promptings of the Divine. This essay identifies twelve Friendly practices, aspects of Quaker process that deepen our worship with attention to business and invite the work of the Divine Presence in our midst.
Discernment – Meeting for Business – Mysticism – Quaker Process – Sense of the Meeting – Unity

454 *The Healing Power of Stories*
Bischoff, Michael (2018)
The author writes movingly about the experience of living with aggressive brain cancer and his experiment of listening to and telling stories of brokenness and healing. The spiritual practice of telling stories can contribute to healing physically, emotionally, and in relation to others.
Cancer – Death – Healing – Spiritual Practices

INDEX BY AUTHOR

Brinton, Howard Haines

Bristol, James E.

Bronner, Edwin B.

Knutson, Jerry

Kylin, Helen

Lacey, Paul A.

Lachmund, Margarethe

Lakey, George

Lampen, John

Landstrom, Elsie H.

INDEX BY TITLE

INDEX BY SUBJECT